E X A M I N[...]
TEXTILES TECHNOLOGY

ANNE BARNETT

Heinemann

Heinemann Educational Publishers
Halley Court, Jordan Hill, Oxford OX2 8EJ
A Division of Reed Educational & Professional Publishing Ltd

OXFORD   MELBOURNE   AUCKLAND
JOHANNESBURG   BLANTYRE   GABORONE
IBADAN   PORTSMOUTH (NH) USA   CHICAGO

First published 1997

01 00 99
10 9 8 7 6 5 4 3 2

British Library Cataloguing in Publication Data
A catalogue record for this book is available from the British
Library

ISBN 0 435 42104 2

Designed, produced and illustrated by Gecko Ltd, Bicester, Oxon
Picture research by Thelma Gilbert
Cover design by Aricot Vert Design
Printed and bound in Spain by Mateu Cromo

Acknowledgements

The author would like to thank Clare Barnett-Thomas and Becky
Poynter for secretarial support; Jilli Blackwood; Johnnie Boden
and Kyle McCrae of Boden; Patricia Bradley, Director of CAPIT B;
Rollo Bruce of BTTG; Melanie Christoudia of The Theatre
Museum; Bob Morley, Marilyn Middleton and Kay Orton of
Courtaulds; Anna Davidson of Wrangler Jeans; Jan Eggleston of
Dylon International Ltd; The Gainsborough Silk Weaving
Company; Flo Hadley, HMI; Jenni Hankins of NES Arnold; Barbara
Bannister, Mary Cooper, Veronica Hartley and Keith Cowell of the
Hebden Bridge Clothing Company; Jo Heeley of Manchester
Metropolitan University; Norma Jacquelin; Jo Jeffrey of Drapers'
Record; Karen Jones of Du Pont; The Liverpool Cotton Association
Ltd; Lyn Luxton of Huso Huso; Janice Markham of Hoechst UK
Ltd; Mr P R Kemp, Thia Richards and Jane Dulieu of Marks and
Spencer plc; Barbara Milligan; Lorna Moffat and the pupils of
Highworth Grammar School; Miss Elsie Long and Sinty Stemp of
Jean Muir Ltd; Emma Orr of the Textile Institute; John Parkinson
of Evergreen; Mr Philip Purkis of the Health and Safety Executive;
Staff of the Education Department of Quarry Bank Mill; Gillian
Rowan-Wilde of J B Broadley; Trevor Rowe of The Bolton Institute;
Helen Houston and Dave Kemp of ScotWeave; Annie Sherburne;
Mr S M Simmonds of Drummond Group plc.

The publishers would like to thank the following for permission to
reproduce copyright material.
Jilli Blackwood for the c.v. on p. 109, the text on p. 110 and the
artwork on pp. 110–11; Boden for the postcard on p. 98 and for
information for the case study on pp. 98–101; The British
Standards Institute for the kitemark symbol on p. 28; J B Broadley
for the redrawn diagrams of a microporous membrane and a
hydrophilic membrane and for the sample of Permatex on
pp. 92–3; The Daily Telegraph for the article on pp. 94–5,
© Telegraph Group Limited, London, 1997; Du Pont de Nemours
International S A and Du Pont (UK) Ltd for the diagrams and
information on p. 49; The Energy Technology Support Unit and
Evergreen for the Crown Copyright material from Energy and
Efficiency Best Practice Programme Case Study 181 (Evergreen),
reproduced by permission of the Department of the Environment
on pp. 73–5; The Gainsborough Silk Weaving Co Ltd for the
brochure cover on p. 121 and for their kind help in the
preparation of the case study on pp. 120–3; Lyn Luxton for the
quote on p. 73; Marks and Spencer plc for the label on p. 105 and
the adapted text on pp. 105–7; Barbara Milligan for the quote on
p. 120; Lorna Moffat for the artwork on pp. 112–16; ScotWeave
and Scot Innovation and Development Ltd for the information and
weave samples on pp. 61–2; Annie Sherburne for the quote on
pp. 117–119; The Textile Institute for the graphs on pp. 9 and 31
and the table on p. 30 taken from Textiles Magazine published by
The Textile Institute; Wrangler Jeans Ltd for the poster on p. 102
and the adapted text and flow charts on pp. 102–3.

The publishers would like to thank the following for permission to
use photographs:
ACE Photo Agency 13tr, 19bl, 22mt, 22tl, 65tr, 77l; Allsport/Mike
Hewitt 22br; Michel Arnaud 94m & r, 95tm, tr, br & bl; Ed
Barber/Annie Sherburne 57t; BMM Weston 81b; Boden 100, 104
(both), 13 br, 23r, 61tl & ml, 99 (all); S Brayne 117r, 119 (all); the
Bridgeman Library/Giraudon 7bl; Burberrys 13 bl; Rab Carrington/
Mountain Sports Photography 93ml & bl; J Allan Cash Ltd 19tr,
77r; Trevor Clifford 22ml, 22mr; Bruce Coleman/David Austen 35b;
Bruce Coleman/Jane Burton 40b; Bruce Coleman/Jane Burton
Dalton 40t; Bruce Coleman/Kim Taylor 40 (2nd bottom); Donald
Cooper/Photostage 90l, 90mb, 90rb, 90tr; Crosrol Ltd 36r;
Haddon Davies/Norma Jacquelin 21t; Dylon 67 (all), 68bl (all);
Electrolux 81m; Energy Efficiency Office, Department of the
Environment 73–5 (all); Gerber Garment Technology 78, 79rt,
80bl, 89lb, 89lt; Robert Harding Picture Library 38; Hoechst
Trevira 53 (both), 71ml, 93br; Michael Holford/British Museum
7br; Chris Honeywell 110 (both), 111, 29, 82l, 83br, 8l; Chris
Honeywell/Norma Jacquelin 87; Jacqui Hurst 84tl & tr; Jacqui
Hurst/Country Living 108, 112, 118bl & br; Hutchison Library 22tr;
Katz Pictures 15r, 77ml; Katz Pictures/Julian Anderson 65rm; LAT
Photographic 48; T Lumb 117l; T Lumb/Annie Sherburne 57b;
Marks & Spencer plc 105–7 (all); Microscopix Photo Library/
Andrew Syred 13 tl, 77m; Mirror Syndication International 13 tl,
77m; Lorna Moffatt 113–16 (all); Jean Muir 96–7 (all); Museum of
London 90mt; Natural Science Photos/G Matthews 83t; Natural
Science Photos/D Meredith 83ml; NES Arnold 68br, 69r; NHPA/
G I Bernard 6; NHPA/Anthony Bannister 35t; NHPA/Stephen
Dalton 40 (2nd top); Panos Pictures/Ben Aris 95tl; "PA" News
Photo Library 23l; Petri Museum of Egyptian
Archaeology/University College, London 7t; Photonews
Scotland/George Wilkie 61br, 62br; Quarry Bank Mill 11 (all); Rex
Features 19tl, 71tl, 77mr; Rex Features/Eric Burley 15l; Rex
Features/Simon Walker 94l; Roger Scruton 33; Science Photo
Library 64; Science Photo Library/Eye of Science 83rt; Annie
Sherburne 118tl; Shout Picture Library 22bl; Simplicity Ltd 84bl;
Spectrum Colour Library 71mr; Still Pictures/Chris Caldicott 71b;
Still Pictures/Mark Edwards 36l; Still Pictures/Muriel Nicolotti 71tr;
Meg Sullivan 120, 122–3 (all); Telegraph Colour Library 18l, 18r,
19br; Tencel® registered trademark of Courtaulds Fibres 47 (all);
Textiles Magazine 8r; TRIP/V Kolpakov 80r; TRIP/H Rogers 69l,
79rb, 80lt, 81t, 89rb, 89rt; Union Special UK Ltd 76; V&A Picture
Library 68tr (both), 83br; Wrangler Ltd 83br, 102 (all).

Contents

Introduction

Achieving success in textiles technology

Textiles technology covers many different areas and manufacturing processes, all of which are covered in this book. However, to achieve success you do not only need to know about the processes and apply them; you must also understand the nature and quality of fibres, yarns and fabrics, and the various techniques used to make them into products. Unless you can demonstrate this understanding, the answers you give in your GCSE exam and the coursework you present for assessment will not score as many marks as you are capable of getting.

The written exam

In the written paper you will be expected to be able to:

- **explain things**
  To do this you must decide what knowledge and skills need to be understood and applied. You do this by selecting the areas which are important to the question being asked, i.e. the relevant areas. Explanations must be accurate and support your judgements and opinions.
- **present and interpret information**
  You must show understanding of the information that is presented and use your ability to work out what it means, i.e. **interpret** it.
- **comment upon the technological actions of other people**
  This means that you must apply your knowledge and experience of the effects of technology, including actions which are successful and those which are not, etc. This type of question could take the form of a **case study**.
- **solve problems**
  Make decisions about situations and other specific suggestions made in the question.

All your recommendations must be supported with reasons based on correct, accurate and relevant material.

- **communicate clearly**
  The examiner can mark only what you write down. You must answer in a way that is appropriate to the question and check that what you want the examiner to know is clearly stated and complete.
- **keep going right to the end of the paper**
  There may be questions you cannot answer: this happens to most people, but do not give up. Make sure you have had a go at the *whole* paper. A minute spent at the beginning of the exam planning your timing is never wasted, because you do not want to run out of time.

Coursework

You will be involved in several types of task throughout your course. These include:

A **short tasks** which are designed to teach you something you did not know, or were not sure about, and need to be reminded about. These help you to gain knowledge and learn how to use it to show understanding, and to use that knowledge in a variety of ways and in different circumstances. They are also useful for learning and practising particular skills which you need to develop for other tasks. These are sometimes called **focused tasks**. In every large task you do, you will need to carry out a number of short or focused tasks, to make sure that your work is the best that you can manage.

B **longer, complete tasks** which are sometimes called **design-and-make** or **capability tasks**. They require you to design and make a product or products for a particular purpose, which may be a special activity or market.

Design-and-make tasks

Before you start this type of task, remember that what you choose to do must:

1 be 'do-able' in your situation
2 be something you are going to enjoy doing; if you lose interest part way through the quality of your work will drop
3 include enough challenges (difficult aspects) within it to ensure you will get the best mark you are capable of achieving. But remember *it must be do-able*.

What skills must be used?

You need to decide what to do, i.e. have a **brief**. The first time you do this you may need advice to help you along. The skills you will be using include:

- **market research**, which will show you what people want
- **analysis of the area of the task**, broken down into manageable parts, e.g. how will the product be used, by whom etc.? What purpose must the product fulfil?
- **developing specifications and criteria** for the task and the product; checking for do-ability, adapting if necessary.

Justifying development

This includes:

- thinking of a number of possible ways, i.e. generating ideas, checked for their appropriateness
- making decisions, giving reasons to explain why they were made
- testing to find out what is best in a particular situation, recording actions and evidence
- presenting design and development ideas
- planning and making
- making and production skills
- measuring actions and outcome to see how well they meet the **criteria** and specifications i.e. **evaluating**

- communication, display, using Information Technology and graphic and other techniques as appropriate.

C The third type of task is **investigating** products. The purpose of this type of task is to find out how things are manufactured, why and for whom. Points **1**, **2** and **3** from B also apply to this type of test. You must be able to:

- describe the product
- find the market it was intended for and the criteria for its development. (You will need to ask questions such as: is the product satisfactory, is it 'fit for the purpose for which it is intended'?)
- find out what the product is made from, how it was produced, the properties of the materials used and how important they are in the successful functioning of the product
- test the product
- evaluate and possibly make suggestions for amendments, further developments etc.

Record keeping

Throughout a course in textiles technology it is essential to research, investigate, analyse and use fibres, yarns, fabrics and processes.

To help you apply and use the information you gather and the opinions you form during the course, you should keep accurate records of all the activities and procedures as you undertake them. Suitable ways of doing this include:

- using a stiff-backed notebook in which information, test results, samples/swatches, etc. can be kept safely
- entering and storing information in files on a computer. Remember to keep back-up files and hard copies in case the computer 'crashes'.

*T*extiles is the term given to all fabrics, whether they are in one piece or made up into garments or other items. Textiles have been used by humankind from the earliest times to fulfil many purposes.

At first animal coats and furs were used to provide warmth and shelter. These were used exactly as they were, apart from some shaping to make them serve their purpose more effectively, for example in order to fit the body more closely or to provide a more effective wind break. The illustrations on the right show examples of the early use of textiles.

When did textiles technology first appear?

Textiles technology began when people found out that the coats of some animals (e.g. sheep) could be used without slaughtering the animal. A method of producing **fibres** was discovered! The photo shows the removal of a sheep's coat by modern shearing methods.

Even from earliest times, some plants, as well as animal skins, were being used to produce **fabrics**. The fibrous quality of plants such as **flax** (linen) made it possible to produce **thread** which could then be **spun**.

■ Early people wore skins and used them to make shelters

How do we know this?

One piece of evidence is provided by the discovery of a deer-antler handle, attached to which are traces of what might be the world's earliest cloth. It was found in a prehistoric village near the River Tigris, in south-eastern Turkey and has been carbon-dated to 7000 BC. It is rare for textiles to survive from this period, which is called the early Neolithic, or New Stone Age. It was at this stage in history when **spinning** and **weaving** were invented. The piece of cloth is about 8 cm by 4 cm, with fine **yarns** (about 0.5 mm thick) spun in clockwise twist (**Z-twist**) and anti-clockwise twist (**S-twist**).

What other examples are there?

Egyptian mummies which have been exhumed (dug up) from their burial ground are found wrapped in bindings of cotton and linen. The Egyptians were combing and spinning flax into threads of various weights and producing fabrics that ranged from coarse sackcloth to fine and

■ Removing a sheep's fleece is a skilled process

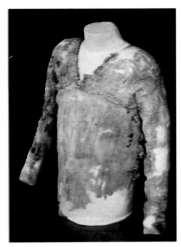

■ **A child's linen dress**

transparent linen from about 2000 BC. The oldest surviving garment in the world is the child's linen dress (shown in the photo), which dates back to around 2800 BC. It is Egyptian and had obviously been worn because it was creased around the armpits and elbows. It was found inside out, having caught around the child's wrists as it was pulled over its head.

When early humans changed their way of life from being **nomadic** (moving from place to place) and started to live in settlements, land was cultivated and domestic spinning, weaving and sewing began. Although spinning and weaving were thought of as women's work, in ancient Egypt there were larger workshops in the towns where fabrics were mass-produced by working men, again examples of early textiles technology. These

workshops became dens of sweated labour. The fabric produced was for the pharaohs, priests and nobles to provide protection, various coverings and adornments.

Clothing design in early Egypt was simple and took into account the effect of the desert sun on the body. A man's basic garment was kilt-like in design, consisting of a piece of cloth wrapped around the body and knotted at the waist. Women tended to wear calf-length sheath dresses which were roughly hemmed and fell from the shoulder or breast. White linen was the most popular cloth because it was light and cool in summer and also offered some warmth when the night air became cold. There is evidence that these people knew how to bleach, starch and pleat their garments. The photos below are examples of fashionable dress worn around 1400 BC.

— *Tasks* —

1 Use the title 'There is nothing new under the sun' for this task. Find modern applications of some of the ideas used by people of earlier times. Sketch the designs you find (or include an illustration which someone else has sketched or photographed) and label the **features** you identify as being the same or similar.

2 Describe in a few words the opportunities offered by your findings for the development of some textile products.

■ (Left) Ancient Egyptians wore simple garments, often made of white linen
(Right) Fashionable dress *circa* 1400 BC

Unit 1.1 showed that people have used textiles and textile products since the earliest times. Methods of production have changed and developed as a result of inventions throughout history, but in fact the reasons why people need, want and use textiles have not changed to any considerable extent.

Some aspects of textile production and use

The study of individual aspects of the production and use of textiles illustrates the extent to which some activities involved are different and some remain the same. Weaving is a simple example. Modern looms are basically the same as the early versions used in many mills in the past. The differences are in the components which have been added for particular purposes over the years. These purposes are most often related to saving time and labour, making possible the production of a more complex fabric, increasing productivity and so on. An early example of a development which created an increase in productivity was the **flying shuttle**, which was similar to the shuttle shown below. This was used in looms for weaving cloth.

The shuttle was propelled (pushed) by hammers in the loom and this made it possible to weave cloth which was wider than the weaver's arms could reach. Before this invention it was impossible to produce wide cloth. Textiles development also brought changes to the living conditions of many people. Saltaire (see box) is just one example.

■ A shuttle used in a loom

Titus Salt (later Sir Titus Salt), who lived between 1803 and 1876, took advantage of the increasing opportunities that the rapidly developing textile industry offered and built a 'model community' to house the people who worked in his mill. This became a company town, called Saltaire. Saltaire is in the north of England, outside Bradford. The town eventually housed around 4500 people and had many public amenities, such as baths, wash-houses, a school, a hospital and a library. These amenities were luxuries to working people at that time and it was the rapid development in textile production and trade which acted as a **catalyst** to improve living conditions.

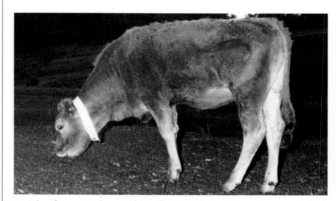

■ A 'road-conscious' cow with a reflective collar

The photo above shows a more recent example of changes as a result of textile production.

Following a series of road accidents in which animals were killed, high visibility collars made from reflective fabric were fitted to cows grazing on pasture lands which cross unfenced roads in some parts of Yorkshire.

Textiles on the Internet

One contemporary example of how people involved in textile production keep themselves up to date is the range of textiles resources available on the Internet. Textiles has a rapidly increasing presence on the Internet with commercial firms, trade and professional associations, educational and research establishments, libraries, individual designers and craftworkers all connected. The

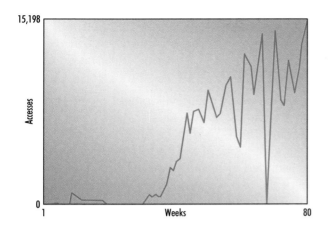

■ The growth in access to textiles information on the Internet

graph above shows the rapid growth of the use of the Internet. The figures show weekly rates of access to the WorldWide Web (WWW) Textiles Page over an 80-week period.

The WorldWide Web provides users with an **interface** to the Internet. It is a collection of inter-linked pages on the Internet which can display pictures, moving video or play sounds. Each site has a specific address (known as a Uniform Resources Locator, or URL) arranged in the format: http:/Internet name/remote path.

The **Internet name** is the name of the server computer and the **remote path** is the pathname for the file you want to read. Http stands for

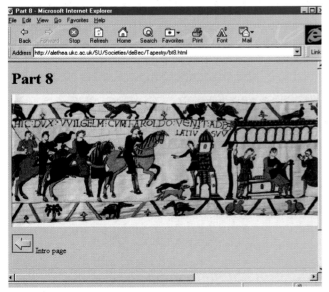

■ Communications – the Bayeux Tapestry on the Internet

Hypertext Transfer Protocol and is what makes it possible to **browse** (scan through) the WWW.

Examples of useful pages for textiles on the WorldWide Web include:

➤ **Bayeux Tapestry** (http://blah.edu/bt) This includes images of 35 different sections of the famous tapestry which show the events which led up to the Battle of Hastings in 1066. These can be down-loaded on to your computer. Close-ups showing stitchings are also available.

➤ **The Fashion Page** (http://www.charm.net/jakec/) This is an on-line magazine giving information about the latest fashions, together with details about fabric care.

➤ **Wool Home** (http://www.woolmark.com) This site contains information about wool and includes processing details from fleece to finished garment. Technical details include fibre properties, such as absorbency etc.

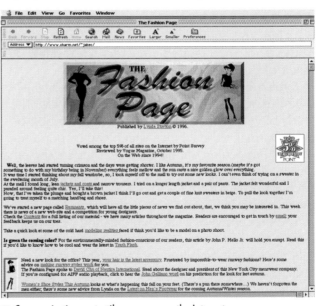

■ Communications – textile resources on the Internet

Task

The Internet addresses shown above may have changed because this technology develops all the time as more people become competent in using it. Carry out your own **research** to discover what up-to-date information about textiles is available on the Internet.

1.3 Is textiles technology new?

The Industrial Revolution

The Industrial Revolution, which took place in the late 18th century, was the start of technological developments which went on for a long time and which have had dramatic effects on textile production.

During the first phase of the revolution, up to 1830, the steam engine was invented in Britain. This was very quickly adapted for use in factories. The second phase of the revolution took place from 1830 to the early 20th century. During this time the internal combustion engine and electricity were developed. These innovations soon made possible more efficient methods of production and distribution of all sorts of goods, including textiles and textile products.

Developments in electronics in the early 20th century and the invention of the **transistor** in the 1950s caused further great changes in industry. Automation of industrial processes became possible. The control systems used in many parts of the textile and related industries are a direct result of these developments.

Cybernetics is the science of how systems organize, regulate and reproduce themselves. The study of cybernetics has led to the production of decision-making machines which can respond to what is happening during particular processes on a factory floor and correct any inefficiency which is occurring. They form the basis of the control mechanisms in use in some factories today.

The processes of both spinning and weaving remain the same as in the past but the machines that have been developed as a result of the Industrial Revolution can make products of better quality, more quickly, in greater numbers and with more variety. Animals and plants have always been used as sources of fibre; the invention of an artificial silk thread (rayon) by Hilaire de Chardonnet in 1889 was the first of many developments of **synthetic** and other artificial fibres. More developments include fibre finishes which allow fabrics to become stain-repellent, fire-resistant, crease-resistant, easy-care, drip-dry etc. Another more recent development is that of **spun-bonded** fabrics. This involves creating a web of fibre (with neither spinning nor weaving involved) and sticking it together by heating it (**fuse-bonding**).

Quarry Bank Mill

One place where the development of the textile industry can be seen is Quarry Bank Mill in Cheshire. This is said to be Europe's largest working museum of the cotton industry. The mill was founded in 1784 by Samuel Greg and it was one of the first water-powered cotton spinning mills. The themes at this museum, which highlight the factors that made the Industrial Revolution include:
➤ an entrepreneur with **capital**, in this case, Samuel Greg
➤ the machinery
➤ the power source (first water and then steam)
➤ the work force.

The effect of the mill on the local people

The history of the mill shows the effect on the surrounding population of such a development. There are strong similarities to what occurred in Saltaire (see Unit 1.2). Samuel Greg founded the mill on this site because of the water power offered by the River Bollin. A series of water wheels was installed, which used this power to drive the mill machinery. In 1818 the 'Great Wheel' was installed. This wheel can be seen at the mill museum. The way the power is taken to the machines (the **transmission** system) is clearly visible from the viewing area. The people who lived in Styal, a small village near the mill, and those from the surrounding area all came to work in the mill. A community was formed, with amenities such as a school, shops and chapels being developed. As the mill increased in size workers came from cities further afield such as Liverpool, many coming from the **workhouses**. They were often very young, aged from nine upwards, and became **apprenticed** (working to learn a craft) to Samuel Greg who provided them with a very small wage, food and clothing. They lived in the Apprentice House and were cared for by

superintendents. Many of the people who live in Styal today are descendants of the apprentices.

Quarry Bank Mill Museum is just one place where technological developments and their effects on the progress of the textiles industry can be seen. There are similar examples concerned with the production of other fibres and fabrics such as wool, silk and manufactured fibres.

What can be seen at Quarry Bank?

There is a display which covers all aspects of cotton, including where it comes from, its qualities compared with other fibres, how it was first spun and woven by hand and the mechanical processes which followed. The scale of the factory as it existed and the processes used to **convert** raw cotton into woven cloth are shown by a team of ex-mill workers. In the weaving shed, production takes place and around 18,000 m (20,000 yards) of cloth are woven annually to demonstrate the

processes which were used at the mill.

There is also a Textile Design and Production Unit which chooses and oversees the processes of bleaching, pre-shrinking, **dyeing** etc. that are done outside the mill. When these processes are completed the cloth comes back to the mill to be made into various products, including lightweight furnishing fabric, **twill** and striped shirtings, blouses, nightwear and toilet accessories. These

— Task

Imagine you have been asked to design and make a range of products which could be sold in a mill shop such as this one.
a What do you think would be suitable?
b Why?
c How could you find out whether your ideas are worth developing?
d Present your findings in a form suitable to show to the curators of the mill.

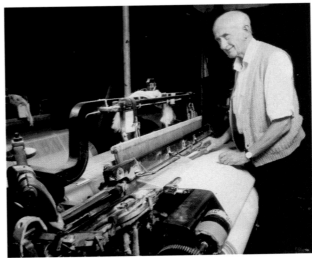

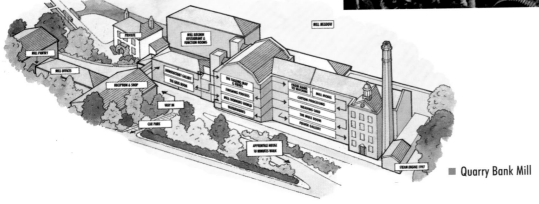

■ Quarry Bank Mill

Processes

The processes involved in production and use of textiles vary. In the textiles industry there are several distinct processes, each carried out by specialist groups of workers. These are:

➤ fibre production
➤ yarn production (converting fibres into yarns)
➤ fabric production (converting yarn into fabric)
➤ dyeing and finishing of fabric
➤ making products e.g. garments (sometimes called **apparel** in the industry), interior furnishings (e.g. soft furnishings, curtains, cushions, wall-hangings etc.).

The study of textiles technology therefore includes:

➤ textile production (i.e. the first four processes above)
➤ making up garments/other items from textiles.

— Task

1 a Look at a number of advertisements (about ten will do) which are intended to encourage people to buy:
   (i) textiles   **(ii)** items made from textiles
  b Make a list of those which fall into group (i). What aspects are referred to in the advertisement?
  c Make a list of those which fall into group (ii). What are the differences between the aspects referred to in these advertisements and those which fall into group (i)?

Things to consider which will help in this task include:
➤ the use of the item being advertised
➤ the people for whom the item is intended
➤ the publication in which the advertisements appears.
Record your findings in your notebook.

Understanding textiles technology

You should now understand that there are two different **sectors** of the industry and that these form the basis for the study of textiles technology. The people involved are either 'textiles people' or 'clothing (other items) people'. The scale to which people are involved in either sector of the industry varies greatly. Some people are designer-makers and specialize in one-off production. Others produce larger quantities ranging from a limited run for a select market (e.g. a few hundred items to meet a particular fashion trend) up to large-scale mass production systems.

Fashion

Fashion may involve making garments or soft furnishings which set the trends for a particular season. These are usually made in very small quantities and are extremely expensive. This is sometimes called **Couture fashion**. (*Couture* in French means 'dressmaking'.) Examples of this sector are given in Section 5.

   Rapidly-changing styles which are not too expensive have created a different type of market in the last 20 years or so. This is a 'young' market for people who want something new, fresh or more in fashion. They are looking for things that are 'of the moment' and not necessarily things which will have a long life. This is generally referred to as the 'street fashion' sector of the market. In garment-making this street fashion caters for both sexes because, in recent years, the interest which most young men have in fashion has increased and now there is tremendous potential for success in the production of street fashion for males as well as females. What other types of clothing are produced?

➤ Garments which have to last the wearer a number of years and are relatively expensive to purchase are examples where a more 'classic' design tends to be chosen (i.e. one which is not the latest trend, more a plain, elegant design which will be appropriate over a number of seasons because it does not look out-dated). A warm coat could be an example.
➤ Garments which are often bought in quantity, such as shirts, underwear, school uniform/wear

are often referred to as **staples** in the industry. The influence of fashion is often less important in the design of such garments and the manufacturer of them can use the same production system and process for a long time.

➤ Garments made in large quantities which have small variations in style are made to display current fashion trends. Many hundreds of thousands of these types of garments are produced, including men's suits, children's clothes, sports outfits, leisure wear, women's suits/clothing etc.

➤ Work-wear (i.e. garments suited to meet the needs of a particular job e.g. nurses clothes, overalls, uniforms etc.).

── *Task* ──

2 a Look at the photos of 'classic' garments. Describe why they are 'timeless' in terms of fashion trends.
  b What special style features do they have? Think about the length of the garment, the colour, the fabric used, etc. Describe each.
  c Imagine that the manufacturer of the classic-style winter coat has asked you to adapt the basic design of the coat to make it appeal to young people. Suggest how you would achieve this. Use sketches and anything else (e.g. a computer) to help you to present your ideas to the manufacturer.

■ Classic clothing

13

1.5 The consumer and textiles

*H*ow does consumer choice affect the variety of textile products on the market?

When people buy things they are making choices based on a number of reasons which fall into groups and can be **categorized**. A very simple categorization would be:

➤ needs
➤ wants.

In this example, there is one fundamental difference between the two categories. N*eeds* are usually products which are essential; *wants* are usually products which satisfy more *emotional* demands, such as the need to buy something, be in fashion, make changes etc.

Choices made in the 'need' category might include:

➤ items of clothing for particular purposes e.g. work-wear used to protect the wearer from a hazard in their job
➤ garments and household textiles which perform particular tasks, e.g. provide warmth, insulation, a barrier from the elements (wind, rain, sun etc.), not to mention clothing which covers the body because it is socially unacceptable to go naked!
➤ items used to carry and transport possessions and goods e.g. bags, hangers etc.

Choices made in the 'want' category might include:

➤ items of clothing, accessories, furnishings etc. which are new designs and/or show up-to-the-minute appreciation of fashion
➤ items which create a particular image which the consumer wishes to project
➤ items which decorate (often referred to as adornments or embellishments in the fashion industry).

More detailed categories which underpin choice can also be developed. These generally include:

➤ performance
➤ price
➤ social, cultural and **aesthetics**.

These categories apply whether the consumer needs *or* wants the product. However, they are not equally important in decisions about which product to choose. Their relative importance depends on:

➤ the type of product
➤ the intended use (e.g. something to be used every day/occasionally, a luxury item, used once only or infrequently and so on)
➤ society/cultural considerations
➤ fashion trends
➤ value for money
➤ resources available for the purchase
➤ individual taste/personal preference.

What are performance factors?

Very simply, these refer to what the consumer requires from the product or textile from which it is made, and what the product and/or the textile from which it is made can do. These factors can be measured, for example, is this fabric waterproof, will this garment crease? How strong is this fibre? They are concerned with technical factors which can be tested and they are used by designers and manufactures to decide how and from what textile an item should be made.

What are price factors?

At their simplest, these ask 'how much?'. However, more complex considerations to do with price include value for money in relation to how the product is to be used.

What are aesthetic factors?

These involve personal taste and judgements, which may or may not be shared with other people. More generally, aesthetic factors are concerned with harmonization, for example, of colours, shapes etc. to provide pleasing and attractive sensations to the beholder or user.

What are the cultural factors?

These can relate to the customs, civilization and achievements of particular people or a particular time in history, or to the arts and other aspects of human intellectual activity.

What are social factors?

These are influences on an individual's choice which may arise from such things as religious customs or the desire to appear like everyone else in a social group. Examples include the Puritans in the 17th century, the Amish Sect in the USA and the 'burka' (veil) in certain Muslim societies. In Western societies such as Britain **peer group pressures** also apply, for example resulting in young adults wearing a particular type of clothing such as blue jeans.

■ Social factors in dress

— Task

a Look at the products below. Categorize them into 'wants' or 'needs'.

b Copy the table and complete it. Give a score of 1 to the factor which is the most important consideration when choosing each product, give the next most important a score of 2 and so on. Do this for all the products.

Products	Factors			
	Performance	Price	Social/cultural	Aesthetics
Umbrella				
Sari				
Ski outfit				
Parachute				
Austrian blind				
Fashion items				

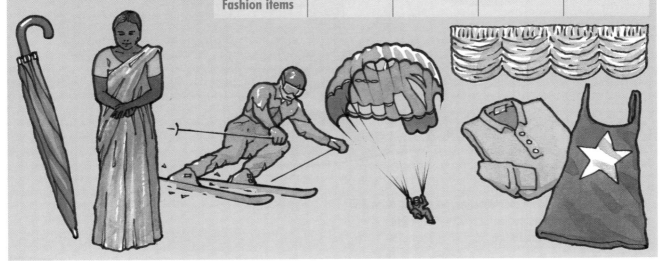

*C*onsumers *buy* products, manufacturers *make* products, retailers *sell* products. Certain things are common to all three of these areas and link them together. **Marketing** is probably the most important of these. Marketing, in some form, influences many aspects of daily life and, if effective, can benefit all those involved: the consumer is satisfied and the producer and the retailer sell their products and are able to continue trading. In marketing terms this is called **satisfactory exchange**.

— Task —

1 a Imagine you are looking for a bag in which to carry sports equipment. Write a list of the features you would expect in such a bag.
   b Look at the drawings of the three bags below and the accompanying descriptions of them provided by the producer. Which bag would better fulfil your needs and expectations? Why?
   c Could the producer have improved the bags you did not choose? Give details.
   d How could the bag you chose be altered to fit your requirements more closely?

A Waterproof hold-all with shoulder strap, 56 × 27 × 24 cm, £30
B Backpack with zip front pocket, 32 × 32 × 22 cm. £40
C Hard-wearing large canvas bag, 56 × 48 × 22 cm, £50

Consumers buy what they require to satisfy their needs and wants but there is no guarantee that a producer and/or retailer can predict accurately what the consumer will choose. Therefore satisfactory exchanges are not always possible. When there is a mismatch between what is produced and offered for sale and what consumers are looking for, the producer and/or retailer suffers financial losses.

The success rate is improved and mismatches are avoided when the producer and/or retailer finds out before production what the consumer is likely to buy. **Market research** is carried out to get information about what the consumer expects from a product, so this also becomes an important link between the three groups mentioned earlier.

Research does not always provide the best evidence about the nature of demand for a product but it helps to reduce the risks of mismatches occurring when products are being developed.

How does marketing work?

All traditional forms of marketing are based on five activities, called the **five Ps** in the industry. These are:
- product
- people
- promotion
- price
- place.

The effect of fashion on marketing

In recent times changes such as technological developments, large ranges of cheap imported goods, the increasing wealth of much of the population and a widening interest in fashion in all areas of life, have meant that marketing has had to become a very important and aggressive aspect of every company's operation. Fashion does not relate only to clothing; there are fashions in all aspects of textile production, including upholstery soft furnishings, accessories.

Research into the 5Ps involves investigating:
- **demographic trends** and the changes in society indicated by them (the study of the figures relating to deaths, births, disease and how they affect communities, where people live and how they live)
- **social trends**
- **lifestyles**
- **working practices**
- **finance** and the ways in which purchases can be paid for
- how the **organizations** which exist for selling and buying are arranged and managed.

Fashion is no longer something that only interests wealthy people. The high streets of the Western world are full of examples of fashion marketing. Marketing fashion today is **synonymous** with marketing a way of life.

Producers and retailers have to make sure that they can make the latest trends available to the consumer in as short a time as possible, when the consumer wants them. The fashion world is **dynamic** and is always changing. If the goods are not available when a particular fashion is popular, the consumer loses interest and sales are lost. Fashions can become out-dated very rapidly. Producers and retailers have developed strategies to ensure that goods are available when they are needed. A computer-based technique called **Rapid Response** is one such strategy. This involves making all the processes involved in production, distribution and marketing as efficient and speedy as possible. The people involved throughout the chain of production and marketing are kept up to date about demand at each stage. This ensures that supplies of component parts and products are available both when and in the amounts in which they are required. The information provided includes feedback about what is required at each stage within the systems used in designing, making, distributing and marketing, to ensure efficiency and speed. Rapid Response is dealt with in more detail in Unit 4.9.

What other information is useful when predicting the type of produce which will be successful?

Forming **profiles** of different types of consumer helps companies to identify the type of product those consumers will buy. Information is gathered about lifestyle and the buying habits of groups of consumers, for example retired people, young people, parents and children. Attention is paid to age, sex, where people live and their occupation, to get an accurate picture. This is called a profile of the market. Having produced a profile of a section of the population, producers and retailers can target the consumer as a potential buyer.

Profiling also identifies niches (gaps) in the market which need to be filled. This is called **niche marketing**.

Profiling consumers has developed partly as a result of work by Abraham Maslow, carried out into the 1950s. Maslow thought that there is an order in which people need and want things, with essential needs such as heat, water, shelter, food etc. coming first, followed by less essential needs (wants) which are concerned with personal fulfilment. He called this order the **hierarchy of needs**. Maslow based this idea on his belief that everyone seeks personal fulfilment and admiration from other people. Niche marketing is an example of how this belief is used.

Mail-order shopping is one example of this type of marketing, where the person who doesn't like shopping, doesn't have time to shop or can't shop for some reason is targeted. There is a case study of a mail order company in Section 5 of this book.

— Task

2 a Look at the photos below and opposite and categorize them to represent different groups of consumers.

A

B

b Write a consumer profile for each group. Include information about their age, sex, culture, interests and type of life as suggested by the pictures. You may want to copy and complete a table like the one below as part of your answer.

c Choose *one* of the groups you have identified. Suggest *one* textiles product you think would sell to this group which could form part of a design-and-make task that could be carried out in school. List the design features in the product you think would appeal to the group. Explain why you think they would find these features appealing.

Photos	Age	Sex	Culture	Interests	Lifestyle
A					
B					
C					

1.7 The function of design

The dictionary definition of design includes words and phrases such as plans, sketches, purpose, establish form of a product, make preliminary pictures/plans/sketches etc.

Designing in textiles technology involves all of those things in relation to tasks being carried out for particular purposes. Those purposes include:

➤ researching, gathering, recording and using information
➤ finding answers to questions, solving problems, e.g. adapting a product which is not entirely successful
➤ meeting challenges such as providing specific aspects of comfort in the manufacture of clothing, meeting the needs of a particular situation using textiles e.g. decorating a textile or textile item in order to produce a special image (such as a company logo, colour or texture interest)
➤ discovering how textile products are made and for what purpose or market they are intended.

The process of design

Designing is not only about having interesting ideas and the ability to invent something new. In fact successful designing can take place only when a sound understanding of all the processes involved in production is applied. This understanding covers:

➤ knowledge of what the market wants/needs: market research provides information which helps to identify products which it may be worth designing
➤ feedback information
  a from manufacturers to show what it is possible to produce efficiently and economically
  b from the market to show what sells well
➤ knowledge of fibres/yarns/fabrics and their qualities; how they can be used, how they react to certain outside forces such as rain, air, cutting, stitching, combining with other materials, heat etc. and the effect which can be created with them
➤ creativity and the ability to develop ideas visually using shapes, colours, textures to produce effective and workable new styles/shapes etc.

➤ knowledge of manufacturing and making processes and techniques
➤ finance, including costing, pricing, the ability to predict the **implications** (financial consequences) of following through a design to production, marketing and retailing.

The stages involved in designing

The garment or apparel sections of the textiles industry are used here to illustrate the stages but in fact the stages are the same for all products.

1 Briefing the designer or designing team

The brief lists details to give the designer some idea of what to aim for. The details include:
➤ the type of product
➤ the age group(s) of the target market
➤ the purpose which the product must fulfil
➤ any specific aspects which must be met e.g. the season of the year/particular climatic conditions etc.
➤ the price range which the product will be in.

2 Research/looking for inspiration and ideas

Almost any train of thought or experience can inspire ideas which help the designer to get started. Some ideas will not be appropriate in terms of the brief but others will be helpful. In Section 5 of this book there are case studies which cover how some designers get ideas.

The following list contains some suggestions which provide inspiration and can be used to promote ideas:
➤ all types of media e.g. films, TV, newspapers, magazines
➤ historical and political events
➤ plays, poetry, novels, autobiographies
➤ machines, fabrics
➤ pop groups, painters.

3 Putting together the collection

A number of ideas which might suit the brief may be considered. The selection of fabrics and the development of any particular theme might take place during this part of the process. Testing may also be carried out to make sure that what is being considered will fulfil the brief effectively.

The testing could be on fabrics, processes or whatever is relevant and needs to be finalized before further development can continue.

A series of sketches often forms part of this testing process, e.g. the front and back view of relevant garments being tried out for appropriateness. **Story-boards** or theme boards are examples of ways in which designers present the collection to other members of the company or customers, e.g. the retailers who are going to sell the product. These boards shows colours and ranges, sketches, textures components/trims etc. to give a visual example of how the designer has interpreted the brief. Suggestions for changes are incorporated before the next stage.

4 Production of a working sketch or drawing

This sketch must contain details of all the special style features: seams, samples of fabric and components/trims etc. from which a pattern and a sample can be made. The designer is always concerned that the proportions of the various parts of the product are in the correct relationship with each other, to create an aesthetically pleasing result, regardless of the type of product.

■ A story-board used in garment design

Task

A company which produces T-shirts has asked you to design a T-shirt which is to be sold at a concert by a popular pop group. The brief states that a named pop group must be used and that the design must:

➤ be in two colours
➤ be 16 cm square
➤ be suitable for uni-sex wear
➤ involve the use of recycled fabric.

Produce a story or theme board which can be used to present your ideas. The photo shows a winning design for a similar T-shirt competition. The design is based on the two letters T and I and shows the up and down and across interlacing of fibres i.e. the **warp** and **weft** of the fabric.

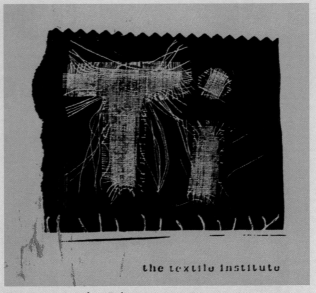

■ A winning entry for a T-shirt competition

The photos on this page show some of the many uses of textiles. Textiles are an important part of our life. In some cases they are used as safety measures, for example, the masks now worn by all racing drivers to protect their faces from fire and smoke, or car tyres which must have the appropriate strength and construction applied to the basic textile used for their production.

Textiles must be **functional**, that is they must perform in the manner required for successful production and end use, whatever textile item is being manufactured.

■ Some of the many uses of textiles

Tasks

1 Look at the photos and list the areas of everyday life covered.

2 List the outer garments you are wearing. Are they all made from the same textile? The answer is 'No' they are not. Compare the type of material needed to make your shoes with the material used to make the top garments you are wearing. What are the differences? Why are these differences necessary? What are the similarities?

Textile qualities

The **qualities** that various textiles possess are determined by the *type of fibre* and the *methods of construction* used in their manufacture. The qualities that can be produced in textiles include:

- strength
- durability
- hard-wearing
- good draping
- absorbency
- porousness
- easy laundering
- flexibility
- elasticity
- non-flammability
- shrink-resistance
- crease-resistance
- resilience – i.e. the ability to resist 'wear and tear' and the ability to go back to the original shape after bending, stretching, pressure (compression), etc.
- anti-static
- warmth or cooling
- water repellence.

Textile properties

Decisions about which textile to use can be made on the basis of the qualities which individual textiles have. These qualities are called the **properties** of the textile. Because these properties are used to design and manufacture (make) successful products they are described as **functional properties**.

— Tasks

3 This outfit (left) is made from newspaper and formed part of an award-winning collection shown at a cancer campaign's recycled fashion show. It is made up of a waistcoat, shirt, tie and skirt. Imagine you have been asked by a manufacturer to copy this design using fabric instead of newspaper.
   a Take each garment in turn and describe the functional properties the fabric must have in order to make the item successfully.
   b Identify and describe the features of this outfit which you think might have helped the designer to win an award.

4 The photo below shows Capri pants, which are fashionable items of leisure wear. What functional properties are needed to make sure these pants look good during activity and movement of the human body?

*C*omfort is another important factor when making decisions concerning textiles and their uses.

What is comfort?

It is easier to describe what comfort is *not*, i.e. what is uncomfortable, because this is a sensation that can be experienced. Comfort tends to be more concerned with the absence of sensations, other than a feeling of well-being. In fact, the *Concise Oxford Dictionary* makes reference to physical well-being in its definition of comfort and gives the example of a warm quilt. The definition of 'comfortable' refers to freedom from hardship, pain and trouble.

— Task

1 What does comfort mean to you? Discuss your ideas with a partner.

What is discomfort?

Discomfort can be defined and measured. When assessing the suitability of a fabric or item of clothing for a particular end-use, it is easier to use terms relating to discomfort because those sensations are identifiable. One way of defining discomfort is to divide the sensations relating to it into two groups.

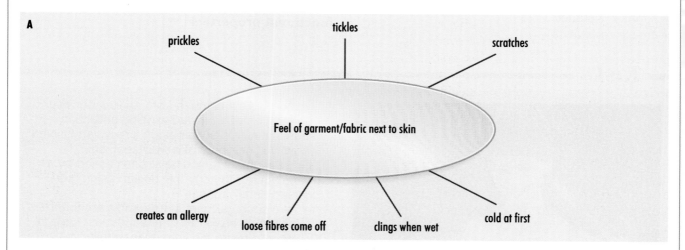

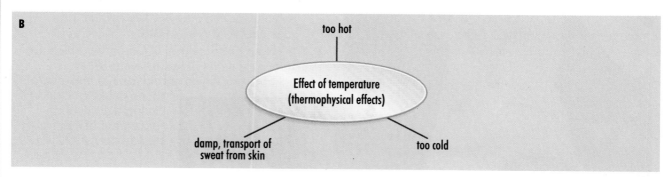

■ Spider diagrams for: **A** Feel next to the skin, **B** Effects of temperature, **C** Fit

One group relates to the effect on the body, i.e. **physical** discomfort. The second group relates to **psychological** discomfort. Physical discomfort can arise from how the fabric or garment feels next to the skin or body. The spider diagrams on page 24 illustrate this in three sections.

Psychological discomfort arises when we feel inappropriately dressed in relation to what other people are wearing, or in a particular situation, or when garments are just not right for us.

Psychological discomfort is also experienced when there is a short-fall in acceptable standards of behaviour and taste. The judgements used are based on aesthetic factors, i.e. what is considered to be pleasing or beautiful to the eye in any particular situation or setting. The spider diagram on this page shows some of the factors from which psychological discomfort might arise.

Avoiding discomfort

Certain aspects of garment construction can create discomfort and these can be referred to in a specification, in order that comfort in use and/or wear are achieved in the final product.

These aspects include:

➤ label types and label positioning. Labels which are placed in a position where there is stress or movement in a garment may scratch or irritate the skin, making the wearer constantly aware of being uncomfortable
➤ bulky, puckering, and wrinkling seams. These can create discomfort and detract from the appearance of a garment
➤ Monofilament polymide threads, which are a known cause of discomfort, especially in a garment which is a 'snug' fit (i.e. a little too tight).

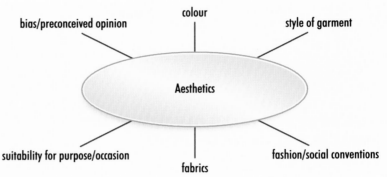

■ A spider diagram measuring aesthetics

— Tasks —

2 Select samples of *four* different fabrics. Identify and describe the qualities of each, using the headings in the spider diagrams which relate to physical discomfort.

3 a The spider diagrams show some of the factors from which psychological discomfort can arise. Imagine you are choosing a garment suitable to wear at an interview for a job. Sketch, model on the computer or cut out of a magazine a suitable garment. Explain why this garment is suitable.
   b Record all your actions in your notebook under appropriate headings.

4 Now consider the same factors in relation to choosing an outfit to wear to a barbecue to be held on the beach in the summer.

*T*he length, **density**, strength, fineness and **elasticity** of a fibre, and its resistance to chemicals, breaking and moisture make it possible to identify the properties a fibre will give a yarn and the resulting fabric.

What does this mean in relation to choosing and using textiles?

The length of a fibre determines the type of yarn which can be produced; for example, the longer the fibre, the smoother the yarn.

The density of a fibre determines the weight of the fabric produced. For example, lightweight fabrics are produced with low-density fibres.

The strength of a fibre is measured by testing its **tenacity**. The tenacity is the breaking force per unit of fineness. The higher the breaking force, the stronger the fibre and the more **durable** the resultant fabric will be.

Elasticity and **extensibility** (resistance to breaking) influence the crease-resistant property of a fabric and its **formability** (the degree to which it can be formed into shapes). Elasticity is measured by the degree to which a fibre recovers its length after being stretched. The degree of elasticity indicates **dimensional stability**, i.e. how much a fibre will shrink or stretch.

Resistance to moisture is dependent on the degree to which a fibre absorbs water. The amount absorbed depends upon the nature of the fibre and the relative **humidity** of the environment. This is dealt with in more detail in Unit 5.1.

How do properties affect the aftercare of textile items?

The care instructions opposite have been developed to provide consumers with the guidance necessary to ensure that they obtain maximum satisfaction and use from the textile goods they buy. The Home Laundering and Consultative Council (HLCC) is the UK National Textile Care Labelling Authority. One of the aims of the HLCC is to develop and promote an International Textile Care Labelling Scheme. This is a system of symbol labelling designed to standardize instructions. It is called the International Care Labelling Code.

The code is based on five symbols. The outlines of these are shown below.

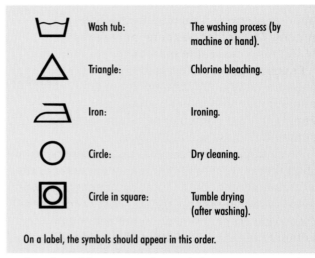

Wash tub:	The washing process (by machine or hand).
Triangle:	Chlorine bleaching.
Iron:	Ironing.
Circle:	Dry cleaning.
Circle in square:	Tumble drying (after washing).

On a label, the symbols should appear in this order.

■ The outlines of the International Care Labelling Code

The washing and ironing applications of the code are shown opposite.

— Tasks

1 a The care instructions appear on other items than textile articles. Find out where they appear. Record the evidence in your notebook.

   b Assess the degree to which your evidence suggests that instructions are standardized. Give examples to support your assessment.

2 Most information on care labels is presented graphically, using symbols with as few words as possible. Why do you think this is? Choose *one* care label and use it to support your answer.

THE WASHING PROCESS

The wash tub symbol when used on its own or in conjunction with a bar or broken bar denotes the following processes:

Symbol		Description of process
⊔	Cotton wash (no bar)	Normal (maximum) machine action and normal spinning.
⊔	Synthetics wash (single bar)	Reduced (medium) machine action and reduced spinning.
⊔	Wool wash (broken bar)	Much reduced (minimum) machine action but normal spinning.

The wash tub symbol should also contain the most effective wash temperature. A full listing of the various wash tub symbols used in the UK, are given below:

Symbol	Examples of applications	Optional phrase
95	White cotton and linen articles without special finishes.	'Wash as cotton' or 'Wash in cotton-cycle' or 'Wash in cotton programme'.
60	Cotton, linen or viscose articles without special finishes, where colours are fast at 60°C.	'Wash as cotton' or 'Wash in cotton-cycle' or 'Wash in cotton programme'.
50	Nylon; polyester/cotton mixtures; polyester, cotton and viscose articles with special finishes; cotton-acrylic mixtures.	'Wash as synthetics' or 'Wash in synthetics cycle' or 'Wash in synthetics programme'.
40	Cotton, linen, or viscose articles where colours are fast at 40°C but not at 60°C.	'Wash as cotton' or 'Wash in cotton-cycle' or 'Wash in cotton programme'.
40	Acrylics, acetates and triactetates, including mixtures with wool, polyester/wool blends.	'Wash as synthetics' or 'Wash in synthetics cycle' or 'Wash in synthetics programme'.
40	Wool, wool mixtures with other fibres, silk.	'Wash as wool.'
⊠	Do not machine wash.	'Hand wash.'
⊠		'Do not wash.'

Symbol	Optional phrase
CL	May be chlorine bleached.
⊠	Do not chlorine bleach.

IRONING

There are four variations on the ironing symbol as shown below:

Symbol	Max. plate temperature	Application	Optional phrase
⌂	200°C	Cotton, linen, viscose or modified viscose.	Hot iron.
⌂	150°C	Polyester mixes, wools.	Warm iron.
⌂	110°C	Acrylic, nylon, acetate, triacetate, polyester.	Cool iron.

■ The washing and ironing applications of the code

*T*here are three types of labels that appear on textile products.

1 Statutory labels

These must appear by law and contain information such as:

a the fibre content of textile products

b **flammability** information such as warnings, together with relevant washing instructions, on nightwear

c flammability warnings on upholstered furniture.

Details

a Fibre content labels must:
  - ➤ use the **generic** name of the fibre (BS4815 is the glossary of generic names for manufactured fibres); the label may also carry the **brand name** or **registered trade name** but the generic name is the only one required by law
  - ➤ give the **fibre composition** of a blend by percentage (%) with the highest first (e.g. 60% polyester 40% cotton); even fabrics bought from a market stall should be labelled like this.

b Flammability labels on nightwear are required by the Nightwear (Safety) Regulations 1985.

c Flammability labels on upholstery are required by the Upholstered Furniture (Safety) (Amendment) Regulations (1983).

2 Optional labels

All other labels are optional. The country of origin is frequently stated but it is not statutory that it should be. Other information that is optional includes sizes and care instructions.

3 Quality assurance labels

These labels show that the product satisfies particular standards. The **kitemark** shown here is an example.

The kitemark is used when the product has been subjected to regular routine testing during production. This is organized by the British Standards Assurance Services.

■ The kitemark

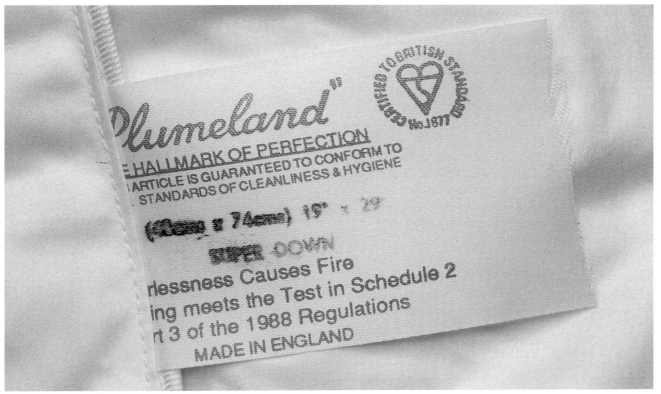

■ A pillow label with the kitemark

The particular British Standard which specifies how a product must perform in use is stated underneath the kitemark.

The function of labels

Labels tell the consumer how to care for a product, by indicating how it should be used and including limitations in use, such as maximum washing temperatures etc.

Manufacturers are very careful about specific washing instructions because it is impossible to predict accurately how individual consumers 'sort' their washing into piles of items, each of which requires the same type of treatment. In fact, some consumers may not 'sort' their washing at all and simply put everything together into the machine and wash on the same cycle. Manufacturers instructions must be very carefully devised in order that they are not held liable for damage which might occur as a result of careless washing or cleaning.

Task

a Find a variety of textile products which carry a particular type of label. What kind of products are they? What are they used for? By whom?
b Find a variety of products which carry the kitemark. What kind of products are they? What are they used for? By whom?

29

Classification and sources

There are so many different fibres in existence that it is necessary to classify them into groups, where each fibre in a particular group has something in common with the other fibres in that group. That common feature can be, for example, the type of source, the method of production and so on. One feature which is common to many fibres is that they are very fine, hair-like materials, Another common feature is that they all have a length many times greater than a cross-section of their width.

A simple classification for fibres is to group them into those which are **natural** and those which are **manufactured**.

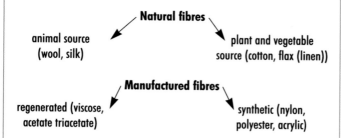

The names shown in brackets in both groups are generic names. These are the names of the type of fibre. Other names are also used to identify fibres of the same type, particularly manufactured fibres. These are brand names and identify the company that produces the fibre. One example is Trevira® which is a polyester fibre produced by Hoechst, a textile company that has its main centre in Germany. Trevira® is the brand name, polyester is the generic name.

A generic name can be written in small letters (i.e. lower case), but when referring to a brand name the first letter should be a capital letter (i.e. upper case).

Fibres can be classified in more detail using the following table which shows the class, type, source and fibre provided.

Classification of principal textile fibres

Class	Type	Source	Fibre
Natural	vegetable	plant seed hair	cotton
		plant base (stems)	flax, jute
		leaf ribs	sisal, manila
	animal	mammalian hair	wool, mohair, cashmere
		larva extrudate	silk
	mineral	silicates	asbestos
Manu-factured	regenerated	wood pulp	viscose
		wood pulp	acetate, triacetate
		natural latex	rubber (elastic)
	synthetic	oil	nylon (polyamide)
		oil	polyester
		oil	acrylic
		oil	polypropylene
		oil	elastane (synthetic elastic)
		oil	chlorofibre (PVC)
	inorganic	silicates, metals metal oxides carbonized MMF	glass, metallic, carbon, etc.

Source: *Textiles Magazine*, Autumn 1994

The diagram at the top of page 31 sets out the classification very simply.

The diagram at the top of page 31 sets out the classification very simply.

Task

1 Carry out research on the names used for some manufactured fibres.
List them in your notebook under the two headings given.

Generic name	Brand name

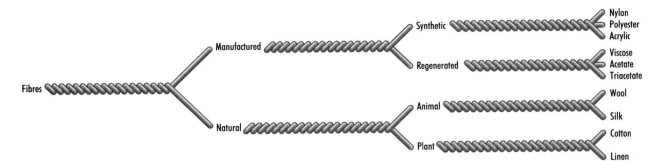

■ Simple classification

Production of fibres

The graph below shows world production of cotton from 1990 to 1992.

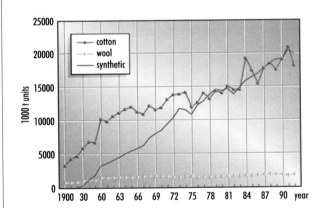

■ World production of cotton, wool and synthetic fibres 1990–2

This graph shows world production of acrylic (PAN), polyamide (PA) and polyester (PES) from 1990 to 1992.

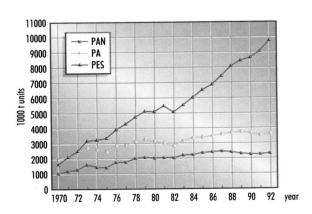

■ World production of acrylic, polyamide and polyester 1990–2

The figures in the second graph show that polyester is a very popular fibre. This is because:
➤ it has lower process costs compared with the other fibres
➤ it has a large number of end-uses, e.g. outerwear, underwear, in domestic and industrial textiles and – very important – in its use with cotton to make a blend of PES/cotton often referred to as polycotton. (This blend is the world's most important blend of fibres.)

— Tasks

2 a Look at a variety of end-uses (products) of textiles. How many of them are made using polycotton? List them.
  b What qualities in each product were required that polycotton fulfilled?
3 a Look at the labels shown below. They each show different amounts/proportions of each fibre. Why?
  b Explain what qualities were required in each case.

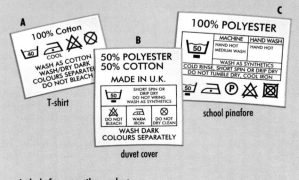

■ Labels from textile products

31

2.6 Cotton

Natural fibres

All natural fibres, except silk, are **staple fibres**. **Staple length** is the typical length of a sample of fibres.

Plant and vegetable fibres

Cotton is a popular fibre which is very **versatile** (can be used in many ways). Just under half of all the textile products in the world are made of cotton.

There are roughly three different qualities, dependent on the staple lengths of cotton fibre. They are:

➤ between 30 and 65 mm – these are top-quality, longer staple cottons such as Egyptian and Sea Island types
➤ between 20 and 30 mm – these are the most common form of cotton and include those referred to as the American upland variety
➤ less than 20 mm – these form coarse, lower – grade cotton and include some of the Asiatic and Indian fibres.

What is cotton?

Cotton is a vegetable fibre, made of **cellulose**, with has a thin coating of wax. Cotton fibre grows as a thin, hollow tube. When it is ripe this collapses into a thin, twisted ribbon. The cotton fibre in the photo is enlarged under a microscope. Notice the twisted ribbon appearance.

What is cellulose?

Cellulose is a **polymer** (several identical units joined together). It is made of many thousands of units of the **glucose molecule**. As many as 10,000 molecules of glucose in a chain may form one molecule of cellulose in cotton. This molecular arrangement can vary which leads to different types of cellulose. Millions of molecules of cellulose make up cotton fibre.

Why is cotton such a popular fibre?

The qualities (properties) which cotton fibre has make it useful in many situations and circumstances. These properties include:

➤ **capacity to absorb moisture** When the wax coating is removed from the fibre during processing the cotton readily absorbs moisture and allows the moisture to **evaporate** (turn into vapour, so that the cotton does not stay wet). This capacity to absorb moisture and then allow it to evaporate makes cotton very comfortable to wear because it allows human skin to breathe, leaving it feeling pleasant and comfortable.
➤ **strength** Cotton is slower to dry than some other fibres. However, cotton fibres are stronger when wet than when dry. This means that most products made from cotton can be washed frequently.

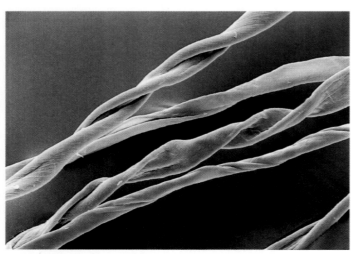

■ A cotton fibre highly magnified

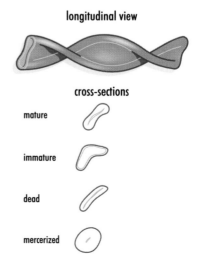

longitudinal view

cross-sections

mature

immature

dead

mercerized

■ Cotton is a versatile fibre

> **minimal build up of static electricity** All fibres acquire small charges of **static electricity** due to friction. Static charge accumulates less readily on cotton than on other fibres, which means that it does not attract dirt or dust to the same extent as some other fibres. The rough surfaces of some cotton yarns, however, mean that fabrics made from them soil more easily.

> **absorbency** Water can **penetrate** the fibre so that dirt can be washed out. Cotton therefore is relatively easy to keep clean.

> **conductivity** Cotton is a good conductor of heat, which is another reason why it is comfortable to wear.

> **good reaction to chemicals** Cotton can be treated with many textile finishes which improve its performance and/or enhance its appearance.

> **versatility** It can be woven and knitted into a wide range of fabrics.

> **other qualities** Qualities/properties such as crease-resistance, shrink-resistance, water-repellence, stain-repellence and flame-resistance can be built in during processing.

> **appearance** Its appearance can be changed easily, for example by bleaching (provided this is done carefully), glazing, embossing, mercerization (treating with caustic soda to increase strength and **lustre** or shine of the fibre).

Disadvantages of cotton

Cotton has the following drawbacks.

> Cotton is not very **extensible** (stretchy) and therefore untreated pure cotton fabric tends to crease badly.

> It tends to turn yellow and be weakened by prolonged exposure to bright sunlight.

> It will scorch if exposed to temperatures above 240°C, so the temperature for ironing must be limited to the hot setting.

> It is damaged by **mildew** and therefore must not be stored damp.

Task

1 a Collect samples of cotton fabric to show the different treatments which are carried out during processing.
  b Arrange them in your sample folder. Include a description of each.

33

■ Where cotton is grown

Where is cotton grown?

About 80 countries in the world produce cotton. They are located on the **latitudes** between 45° north and 30° south, where 175–225 frost-free days can be expected each year. The map shows the areas in the world where cotton grows. There is worldwide trade in cotton, said to be worth billions of dollars every year. The figures in the graph show typical proportions of the use of cotton.

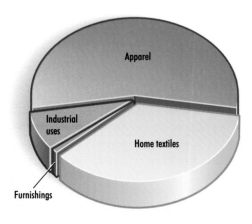

■ The use of cotton

How does cotton grow?

Cotton grows on bushes which need hot weather, sunshine and moisture to produce a good crop. Cotton needs a warm, **humid** climate with good **irrigation** (an adequate supply of water). Growing conditions are ideal when there is a period of about six months when the temperature is mild, with about 12 hours of sunshine per day, followed by a period of wet weather when there needs to be up to 50 cm of rain (at least 8–10 cm per month) or an irrigation system which provides a similar level, followed by a dry period when the fibres are maturing. If these conditions are not met the cotton crop suffers and a shortage results. Any serious shortage can result in a rise in the price of cotton on the world market.

What happens during growth?

The fruit capsules of the cotton plant burst when ripe. Inside is a fluffy mass of creamy-white fibres. These are the long, silky hairs on the surface of the seeds. The seed case is called the **boll** and this is what is picked. The photo at the top of page 35 shows the cotton seed bolls on the plant.

■ Cotton seed bolls on a cotton plant

Harvesting

Cotton always used to be picked by hand, for example, by slaves in the southern states of what is now the United States of America. (The life and development of slaves provides an interesting study and is another example of the effect which textile production has had on some people's lives.) Now machines are used to harvest the crop in most countries. The photo at the foot of this page shows a mechanical cotton picker.

Ginning

The fibres are separated from the seeds by a process called **ginning**. Gins are machines made specially for this purpose. A saw gin or a roller-type gin is used, depending on the type of cotton. For example, for Sea Island and Egyptian-type cotton, the roller type is used and for upland-type cotton (notably the American type) the saw gin is usually used. Ginning takes place in the country of origin. The fibres are then packed into **bales** and sent to a mill. The seeds are used to make cotton seed oil and **protein**-rich animal feeds.

― Task ―

2 Design a leaflet which gives consumers information about cotton production and use.

■ Cotton is now picked by mechanical cotton pickers in many parts of the world

■ Baling cotton in Cameroon

At the mill

The processes involved in yarn production are described below.

1 Opening

The cotton is opened, to remove sand, grit and any other impurities. Openers have a beating mechanism which loosens the fibres and separates the impurities from the fibre. The fibres are then blown against a perforated drum to remove the sand and grit etc.

2 Scutching

A scutching machine continues the cleaning process by further beating and then it rolls the fibre into sheets (**laps**), ready for the next stage of production.

3 Carding

A carding machine consists of rollers which have pointed wires sticking out from the surface. Carding is like a combing process. The wire points pull the cotton fibres to make them parallel to each other and then separate them, making a web-type structure. The fibrous web then forms a **sliver** (rope). The friction from the fibres holds them together at this stage.

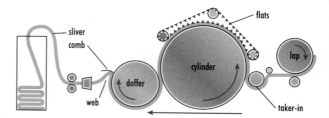

A roll (lap) of cotton is placed onto the carding machine.

The carding machine:

➤ opens the cotton to single fibres
➤ removes trash (leaf, stalk, broken seed, sand)
➤ removes short fibres and tangled fibres.

The cotton is taken from the doffer as a thin layer of fibres (web) which is funnelled into a rope-like sliver.

■ A row of carding machines in a factory. The diagram above the photo shows the basic carding process

4 Drawing and drafting

The thickness of the slivers is reduced by **drawing** and **drafting**. These processes are carried out using a series of sets of rollers, each set working faster than the previous one. The processes make the slivers more regular and fine enough to spin into yarns.

5 Spinning

This is the final process of the yarn production sequence. There is a cotton-spinning system which was developed especially for spinning cotton. It is based on what is called **ring spinning**. In ring spinning, when the roving leaves the final drafting rollers it passes through a hole, called a **pot eye**, and under a small ring, called a **traveller**, to the **bobbin**. The bobbin turns on a **spindle** and the resulting yarn is evenly wound around it. The yarn is twisted during this process. Cotton can take a very high twist which makes it stronger.

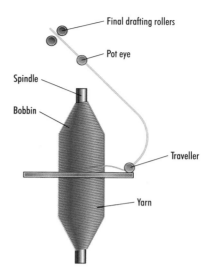

■ The ring spinning of cotton

The next process is the production of cloth from yarns. Two processes are involved, they are weaving and knitting. These are covered in Unit 3.4 (page 58) and Unit 3.6 (page 63).

Did you know?

Your old cast-off denim jeans could end up as money in somebody's wallet! Tons of regenerated cotton rags and high-grade spinning waste are used to make the special paper for banknotes. The paper manufactured from cotton fibres is stronger and better able to withstand the handling which currency notes get. Other outlets for 'rag paper' include legal documents, certificates, maps and other products where the paper is subjected to hard wear and frequent folding.

Cotton fibre waste has also been used to help clean up oil slicks at sea. Research workers in Japan and the USA have developed techniques for recovering the oil by trapping it in raw cotton fibre which, because of its natural waxes, does not absorb water readily and can remain afloat.

— Task

3 For this task you will need:
  ► your notebook and sample/swatch-book
  ► 2 samples of pure cotton fabrics
  ► a hand lens
  ► a dissecting needle
  ► a ruler
  ► a microscope.
  a Look at the samples first with the naked eye and then through the hand lens. Write down what you see in each case.
  b Remove individual fibres from each sample and examine them using first the hand lens and then a microscope. Write down what you see in each case.
  c Draw the shapes of the fibre which you see under the microscope.

In this task you have taken something apart in a very simple way. This is sometimes called **disassembly**. The purpose of taking things apart is primarily to find out what they are made from and how they were produced. An important aspect in the study of textiles technology is discovering why and how textiles and textile products are made.

*L*inen fabric is produced from the fibre of the flax plant. Flax is an **annual** plant, which means that it must be sown every year. The growing conditions required are provided in areas where there is a **temperate** (mild) climate. The seeds are planted in March and April and take 90–120 days to grow. Flax is grown for either its seed or its fibre. For fibre, tall varieties are needed. These grow to about 80–120 cm and have whitish, light blue flowers which grow at the top of the stem of the plant. After flowering a **seed capsule** develops which is very rich in oil. Flax fibres are extracted from the stalks of the plant. Harvesting takes place in July and August.

Producing areas

Around 20 countries in the world grow flax. The main ones are China, Russia, the Ukraine, France, Belarus, the Netherlands, Egypt, Lithuania, the Czech Republic and Belgium. These countries are shown in the map on this page.

The amount of flax produced in the last 20 years has been fairly constant, at 600,000–700,000 tonnes. This is about two per cent of total world fibre production.

■ Where flax is grown

How is the fibre extracted?

The stages involved are described below.

1 Pulling

The flax plant is harvested whole, to obtain the full length of the fibre. Machines are used to harvest the crop; the process is called pulling.

2 Roughing out

This removes all the seeds and other unwanted material from the stems.

■ Harvesting flax

3 Retting

This process loosens the fibres by breaking down the woody part of the stems and dispersing the sticky substance which holds the plant together. Retting is carried out in one of two ways. Either the harvested flax is left lying in the dew of the field for a few weeks or the flax is put into tanks of warm water and left there for a few days.

4 Breaking and scutching

The flax straw is crushed and beaten to separate the fibre from the woody bark. Fibres about 45–90 cm long and woody parts called **scutcher tow** (about 10–25 cm long) are produced.

5 Hackling

The fibres are combed during this process to produce long **line** fibres which can be spun. This is called **line flax**. The short fibres which are combed out are removed and are called **hackle tow**.

6 Processing

The line flax is spun into yarns using a method of wet-spinning called the **linen process**. The yarn produced is very fine and regular in shape and is used in clothing (apparel) fabrics and those fabrics used for high-quality household textiles. The shorter fibres, the hackle tow, are spun by a dry-spinning method and produce heavier yarns suitable for use as furnishing fabrics, wall coverings, tea-towels, canvas etc.

Why is flax a useful fibre?

The properties which flax possesses meet many of the requirements built into the specifications for fabrics and their uses. These properties include:

➤ **moisture absorption** Flax (linen) absorbs water very quickly and also releases it very quickly into the surroundings. This means that linen fabric is comfortable to wear in hot weather in that it helps to regulate the difference in temperature between the body and the hot surroundings (the **micro-climate** between body and clothing).

➤ **thermal insulation** Flax fibres do not trap (enclose) much air and therefore impart a cool feel, which is an advantage in hot weather.

➤ **strength** Flax is a strong fibre and increases in strength when wet. It makes a very durable fabric (i.e. linen) which is hard-wearing. It has a high **tenacity** value.

➤ **low level of static charge** The fibre always contains some moisture, therefore static charge is almost non-existent.

➤ **resistance to soiling** Flax has a smooth surface and little gloss, which means that the linen fabric made from it does not soil easily; it can also withstand high temperatures without the risk of spoiling e.g. white pure linen fabric can be boiled at 95°C.

Other properties

➤ The low extensibility and elasticity of flax fibre mean that linen fabric creases very badly. However, these properties mean that because of its low stretching quality when under tension it can be used for parachute harnesses!

➤ Flax fibres are stiffer and harder than cotton fibres and the fibre bundles are coarser. This gives linen a lack of suppleness (ability to bend/be flexible).

➤ Properties can be improved by finishing techniques such as crease and flame-resistance and water-repellence.

— Task

For this task you will need:
➤ your notebook and sample/swatch book
➤ 2 samples/swatches of pure linen fabric
➤ a hand lens
➤ a dissecting needle
➤ a microscope.

a Collect samples/swatches of pure linen fabric. Examine them first with the naked eye, then with the hand lens. Make notes about what you have seen.
b Remove individual fibres from the fabrics, using the dissecting needle and examine them as in a above. Make notes about what you have seen.
c Examine one of the fibres under the microscope. Draw the shape of this fibre.
d If possible, compare the flax fibre and linen fabrics with the cotton fibre and fabrics you used in the task on page 37.

S ilk is an animal fibre but it is not a staple fibre. It is obtained in a thread-like form, and is a **filament** fibre. Silk production is called **sericulture**.

Sources

The most important silk producing areas include China, India, Japan and the former USSR. About 70,000 tonnes are produced worldwide annually. This is less than 0.2 per cent of the world's textile production. The map on this page shows the main area of production.

What is silk?

Silk is a fine, soft thread produced by the larvae of the silk moth. The most common cultivated species, *Bombay Mori*, is the one usually used for sericulture. The worm or larva grows to maturity within a month of hatching from the egg. During this time it feeds on mulberry leaves and spins a protective cocoon of fine, silk thread. Glands in the silk-worm produce two different liquids which make the cocoon. One is fibrous (a protein called **fibroin**) and the other is gum (**sericin**). A mixture of the two liquids is **extruded** from two horns in the silk-worm's head and this is what produces the filaments. The silk-worm attaches these sticky filaments to a twig or frame. Then, by moving its head in a figure of eight motion, the silk-worm wraps itself in the cocoon, spinning from the outside inwards.

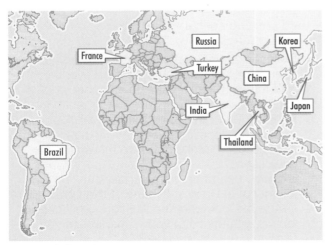

■ Areas of silk production

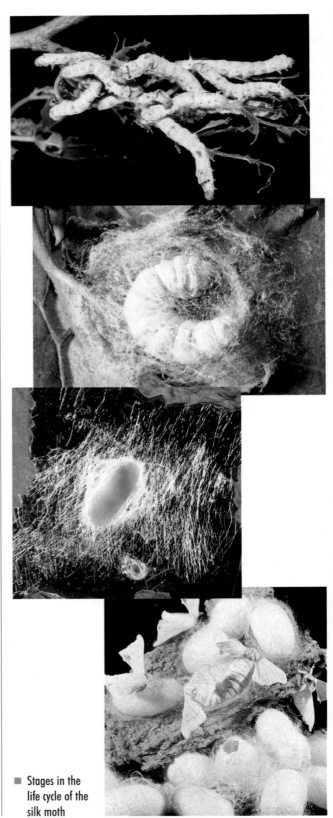

■ Stages in the life cycle of the silk moth

Obtaining the fibres

In commercial production the silk-worm eggs are hatched on trays which are spread with mulberry leaves. Before the **pupa** (chrysalis) is able to emerge as a moth, the cocoons are subjected to either dry or wet heat which kills the insect. The cocoons are put in a bath to remove the gum, then the ends of the filaments are found and are unwound with the help of a revolving brush. A single filament is usually too fine to make a yarn so a number of cocoons (usually 3–8) are unwound and put on reels together to make a single yarn.

If the pupa is left to develop into a moth, it dissolves part of the cocoon and escapes in order to mate. The female moth lays the eggs and then dies and the whole process starts again as more silk-worms emerge from the new eggs.

Types of silk

- **Raw silk** This is made from up to ten undamaged cocoons wound together. This is sometimes called **greige silk**.
- **Spun silk** This is spun from unwindable parts of the cocoons, together with other waste silk. Long raw fibres are cut to maximum lengths of 30 cm and spun.
- **Dupion silk** This is made from double cocoons where silk-worms have spun their cocoons together; the thread produced is uneven and thick.
- **Tussah silk** This is produced from uncultivated silk-worms. It is not easy to de-gum and the fineness of filaments varies.

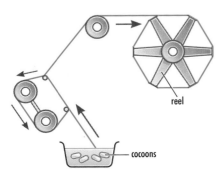

reel

cocoons

■ Obtaining the fibres

The properties of silk

- ➤ The fine fibres produce compact fabrics which can trap air around the body. This air is warmed by body heat and, because it cannot escape easily, keeps the body warm. It is this action that gives silk the reputation of having high **thermal insulation** properties.
- ➤ Having high moisture absorption, silk can absorb and hold up to one-third of its weight in water vapour without feeling wet.
- ➤ The fine, soft feel makes silk comfortable to wear.
- ➤ It is very strong because the fibre has a high degree of tenacity.
- ➤ It has a high degree of elasticity which makes it a **resilient** fibre that resumes its shape quickly after being stretched (although this varies to some extent in relation to the type and weave of the silk).
- ➤ It has a high resistance to static electricity; because it always contains moisture there is usually little electrostatic charge.
- ➤ It is very easily spoiled by chemicals used in some products. For example, some deodorant sprays and perfumes can bring about colour change, as can **perspiration**.
- ➤ It can have its properties improved by finishing processes; for example the removal of the sericin gum by gentle boiling in mild soap solution (called de-gumming) makes knitted and woven raw silk softer. The de-gummed silk is then weighted by the addition of chemicals such as metallic salts.

▬ Task ▬

Carry out some research into silk products on the market. Find out about:
a the variety of products available
b the claims made about three to four different products (e.g. shirts, dresses, cushions, curtains) etc.
c the prices charged
d the type of retailing outlet (type of shop, mail-order)
e details on the label of each product, including reference to fibre and percentage, care advice.
Record your findings in your notebook.

What is wool?

Wool is a staple fibre obtained from the **fleece** of sheep. The sheep are **shorn** to remove their coat. It is this coat which is the fleece. Wool is a protein fibre made up of molecules of **keratin**. The long-chain proteins make small fibres called fibrils which are arranged together in bundles, called fibrilar bundles. These bundles make up the cells of the fibre which are called spindle cells.

The inside of the fibre reacts to water and temperature differently to the outer layer of the fibre. What happens is that they swell to different extents, causing changes in the overall fibre shape. The effect of this is that wool gives good shaping and smooth qualities which can be used to meet particular performance requirements.

Classification of wool

There are hundreds of types and breeds of sheep which are classified according to the wool they produce. There are five basic types of wool:

➤ **Fine** – which comes primarily from Merino and Ramboillet breeds. These give fibres 50–120 mm long which are highly crimped (wavy).
➤ **Medium** and **Crossbred** – these two groups share similar characteristics. The fibres are medium, 120–150 mm long with a normal crimp.

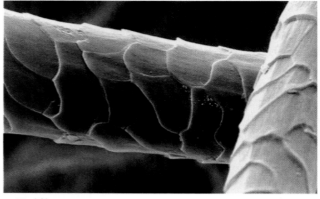

■ Wool fibres

The main varieties of sheep which provide this type of wool include Southdown and Corriedale.
➤ **Long** and **Coarse** – these two groups also share similar characteristics. The fibres are coarse and about 150 mm long. The main varieties of sheep which provide this type of wool include Lincoln, Romney and Karakul.

Where does wool come from?

The map at the bottom of this page shows the major wool-producing areas of the world.

The properties of wool

➤ **Capacity to enclose air**
The fibres with a large degree of crimp can trap a large amount of air which provides warmth. Fine, combed yarns enclose less air and are cooler to wear (sometimes referred to as cool wool).
➤ **Capacity to absorb water**
Wool can absorb up to one-third of its weight in moisture/vapour without feeling wet. It does, however, dry very slowly.
➤ **Elasticity** Wool has a high degree of elasticity which means that it **drapes** well and that creases drop out very quickly.

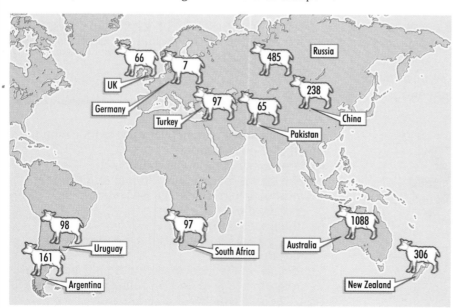

UK 66
Germany 7
Russia 485
Turkey 97
Pakistan 65
China 238
Uruguay 98
Argentina 161
South Africa 97
Australia 1088
New Zealand 306

■ Wool-producing areas of the world (millions kg greasy wool)

➤ **Soft feel** Depending on the fineness of the fibre, wool usually feels soft. Fine Merino wool is especially soft.

➤ **Strength** The wool fibre is not as strong as some other fibres, therefore wool fabrics are not always the best choice when hard-wearing quality is required.

➤ **Stretch** It is a very extensible fibre and easily stretches out of shape when wet.

➤ **Felting** The scales on the outside surface of the fibre hook into each other when subjected to damp heat. This can cause **matting (felting)** which can be a disadvantage in the washing of woollen products.

➤ **Low static charge** Wool produces very low levels of electrostatic charge because the fibres always have a degree of moisture in them.

➤ **Low flammability** Wool does not burn easily (it has a low degree of flammability).

➤ **Treatment** Its performance can be improved and its properties changed by various treatments including mothproofing, permanent creasing, water-repellence etc.

The processing of wool

1 Grading and sorting

Fleeces are graded for quality after shearing. The criteria used are fineness, crimp, length, impurities and colour.

2 Scouring

During this process the fleeces are opened up and washed in a series of tanks containing, firstly, detergent and a mild **alkali** through to the last one which contains rinsing water. The dirt and most of the grease are removed during this process.

3 Carbonizing

This is to remove all vegetable impurities. They are burned away by acid (usually sulphuric or hydrochloric acid) but the wool itself is not affected by the treatment.

4 Carding (combing)

The fibres are **carded** (combed) in a carding machine to make slivers which are uniform in quality and weight. The long fibres are separated from the short fibres. The long fibres are called **tops** and the short fibres are called **noils**.

5 Spinning

Different yarns are produced according to the type of fabric to be made.

a For **worsted**, a smooth, round yarn of parallel fibres is required and the best quality fleeces are used for this. The crimp of the fibres is reduced before spinning to make it easier to make them parallel. The spinning of worsted yarns is carried out mainly on a ring spinner (see page 37). Worsted is used for making suits and other high-quality garments.

b For woollen yarns the woollen spinning method is used. Woollen yarns are heavier than those used for worsted and have many uses including knitwear, coats etc. Yarns with a high bulk are produced by not aligning the fibres to any great extent and by giving a lower twist to the yarn.

The worsted and woollen spinning systems are not only used to spin woollen fibres. For example, they can also produce polyester woollen spun yarn and a polyester worsted spun yarn.

━ *Task* ━━━━

You will need:
➤ your notebook and sample/swatch book
➤ a hand lens
➤ a dissecting needle.

a Collect a small sample of woollen fabric and a small sample of worsted fabric.
b Compare the two by:
examining the feel of each
looking at each with the hand lens
peeling away a few fibres from each sample, examining a single fibre from each sample with the hand lens.
c Mount the samples and fibres you have used in your notebook and record your findings.
d Write a short comparison using the evidence you have collected.

*A*lmost half of all the textile fibres used throughout the world are manufactured. The key to their success is based on the fact that they can be produced in forms and with properties and characteristics to suit particular purposes.

How is this done?

The three processes involved in the production of all manufactured fibres are:

➤ converting (changing) a fibre-forming substance into a fluid, by melting or by making a solution by dissolving the material from which the fibre is to be made into a viscous (thick) liquid
➤ forcing or extruding the liquid through tiny holes in a spinneret
➤ changing the extruded filaments into a solid, i.e. **solidification**.

Put very simply this is rather like forcing a treacle-like material through the rose of a watering can,

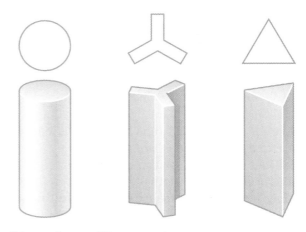

■ Spinneret shapes and fibre cross-sections

■ The extrusion process

and then immediately solidifying the thin streams which appear. The extrusion process is shown in the diagram to the left.

Modern manufacturing methods are more sophisticated and complex.

1 The plate or die through which the liquid is forced (the spinneret) is made up of thousands of precision-drilled holes. The viscous liquid being forced through is called the **dope** or **polymer**. The performance properties and the characteristics of the fibres can be determined by the raw materials used to produce the polymer. Modifications can be made to the polymer before it is put through the spinneret if it does not meet the specification for the end-product. For example, colour agents can be added and anti-static, flame-retardancy and other properties can be built in. Sometimes the shape of the holes in the spinneret is altered to make fibres with a special cross-section for particular purposes. For example, carpet fibres are sometimes given a special cross-section to preserve the appearance of the pile.

   The diagrams above show examples of spinneret shapes and the resulting fibre cross-sections.

2 Once extrusion and solidification have taken place the filaments are stretched under tension to produce strong and uniform fibres. This is called **drawing**.

   Groups of filaments may be twisted together to form a continuous yarn. To make shorter

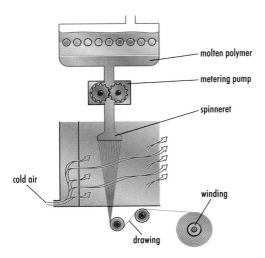

■ Wet-spinning

lengths, a bundle of filaments (called a tow) are first crimped and then cut to make them like natural fibres.

The following terms are used to describe manufactured fibres.

➤ **filaments** These are continuous strands of manufactured fibres.
➤ **mono-filaments** These are made when the spinneret has a single hole only.
➤ **multi-filament** This is a bunch of filaments produced when the spinneret has a lot of holes.
➤ **textured** These are multi-filament yarns which have been given a treatment which bulks (make it seem thicker) and crimps (makes wavy).

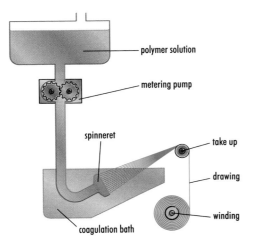

■ Dry-spinning

3 Three main types of spinning processes are used for manufactured fibres. They are:
➤ wet-spinning
➤ dry-spinning
➤ melt-spinning.

This is what is involved in each case.
Wet-spinning The polymer solution is extruded into a bath which contains chemicals which neutralize the solvent (dissolved fluid) and solidifies the filaments.
Dry-spinning The polymer solution is extruded into a stream of warm air which evaporates the solvent and solidifies the filaments.
Melt-spinning The polymer is put into a bath as chips or granules and is melted before being forced through the spinneret, the molten (melted) polymer is extruded into a cold stream of air which cools the melt and solidifies the filaments. The manufacturing process can be programmed to produce fibres with particular properties and characteristics which remain exactly the same in every batch of fibres produced.

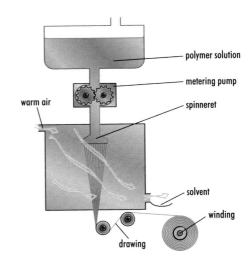

■ Melt-spinning

— *Task* —

Design a leaflet which contains information for the consumer about manufactured fibres.

45

Regenerated fibres are made from wood pulp. Cellulose is dissolved from the pulp and a viscous (thick) liquid is produced. This is what gives one of the fibres, **viscose** its name.

The process

1 The raw material comes from trees. The bark is removed and, after various processes, the cellulose obtained is purified, bleached and then pressed into solid sheets.
2 The cellulose is dissolved in caustic soda (sodium hydroxide), making soda cellulose.
3 Excess liquid is removed and the soda cellulose is shredded and left to age. This reduces the length of the cellulose molecules which makes them dissolve more readily.
4 Carbon disulphide is added (**xanthation**) which changes the cellulose into a fluid which can be dissolved in dilute sodium hydroxide. This is the spinning fluid; it is thick and treacle-like in appearance.
5 The fluid is then filtered and extruded into a spinning bath where the filaments solidify and are washed to remove process chemicals. They are then drawn into a filament yarn which is wound onto a spool or cut into lengths to make staple fibres.

Modal is another regenerated fibre which is made by a slightly different process. The fibres produced are stronger.

Acetate and triacetate are two other regenerated fibres.

— Task

1 a Collect one sample/swatch of:
   (i) a fabric which contains viscose
   (ii) a fabric which contains modal.
  b Mount these in your notebook and include a brief description of the appearance, feel and use of each of them.

Case study: An environmentally friendly cellulose fibre

Courtaulds is a large company that started the manufactured fibre industry by commercializing the viscose process.

Courtaulds and the 'Genesis project'

Courtaulds launched this project, the objective of which was to develop a cellulose processing system which did not harm the environment in any way. The result was the production of a new type of cellulose fibre using renewable wood pulp as the source, produced by a new 'closed loop' spinning process using a non-toxic solvent which is continually recycled. The fibre was called 'Lyocell' and in 1989 the *Bureau de la Standardisation de Fibres Synthetiques* (BISFA) adopted lyocell as the generic name for solvent spun cellulose fibre.

In 1992 Courtaulds launched their particular lyocell fibre for use in fashion apparel products. This is called TENCEL®. TENCEL® is Courtaulds' registered trademark for lyocell when it is used for apparel.

This fibre is protected and promoted through Courtaulds Branding and Quality Assurance programme. If a garment manufacturer wishes to use TENCEL® swing tickets or sew-in labels, or if a designer wishes to develop a special TENCEL® collection, then their garments must be made from certified fabrics. (These carry a TENCEL® quality (TQ) number).

Courtaulds' lyocell has been developed by the company for use in technical textiles such as protective clothing e.g. work-wear, tents, breathable fabrics (for example, non-wovens) to make swabs and dressings for medical use, hygiene wipes, and pads and for special papers, for example, tea bags.

Labelling

Garments made from lyocell, even those branded TENCEL® should carry a composition label bearing the fibre's generic name, as shown here.

100% lyocell

■ A composition label

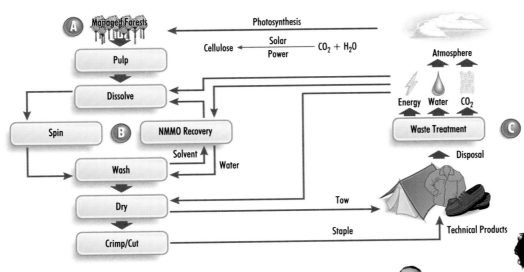

■ The lyocell life-cycle

Details of the process

The new solvent process used to produce lyocell is shown in the diagram. Notice the circular direction of all the arrows, this shows a system which continuously circulates, otherwise known as a closed loop system. In this case the part of the process labelled C illustrates the environmental benefit of this system in that nothing is wasted and the whole process is self-regenerating.

What is the TENCEL® kiss?

This is a reference used by Courtaulds to describe the 'feel' of fabric made from TENCEL®. They say that there is a feeling of well-being created between garment and wearer. The photos show examples of the use some designers have made of TENCEL®.

— Tasks

2 Choose *one* of the designs shown and analyse the qualities which the fibre gives to the garment.

3 Examine the possibility of using a fabric containing TENCEL® in a design-and-make activity carried out in school. Consider price, functional characteristics claimed for the fibre and the performance characteristics required in the item to be made.

■ Uses of TENCEL®

Polyester, polyamide, aramids acrylic and elastane are synthetic fibres. They differ from regenerated fibres in that the polymers from which they are made are artificially produced. (Remember, polymers are several identical units joined together, see page 44). Even so the materials from which the polymers are made are oil and coal. The polymers are made by synthesizing (joining together) simple chemical compounds which come from those natural sources, hence the name 'synthetic fibres'.

Polyester

Polyester is said to be the most versatile of all manufactured fibres because it has the widest range of uses. Sixty per cent of polyester production is in the staple fibre form. The production of filament fibre form is about forty per cent.

Production method

1 Chemicals from oil are joined together to make the polymer.
2 The fibre is melt-spun through spinnerets which are designed to produce fibres of the required type and fineness. The fibres solidify in the air.

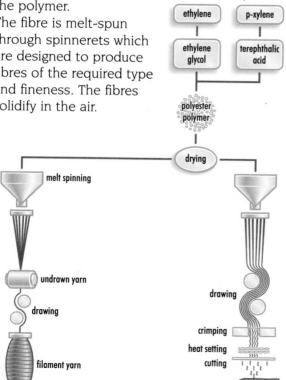

petroleum — ethylene — ethylene glycol

petroleum — p-xylene — terephthalic acid

polyester polymer

drying

melt spinning

undrawn yarn

drawing

filament yarn

drawing

crimping

heat setting

cutting

staple fibre

Labelling

Polyester is a common noun, in this case a generic term. There are, however, many brand names which are used to describe the fibres/fabrics produced, including Terylene® (ICI), Dacron® (DuPont), and Trevira® (Hoechst).

Polyamide

Nylon, an important polyamide, is produced in two ways. The first method, which was discovered in 1935 by an American called Carothers, produced the very first synthetic fibre which was made from coal. The method involves a reaction between two compounds to form the nylon polymer. This type of nylon is called **nylon 6.6**. The second method involves one compound which can make the polymer by linking up with itself. This is called **nylon 6**. These two types of nylon differ slightly chemically but the properties they give to fabrics are almost identical. Nylon is produced mostly in filament form, and today is usually made from oil rather than coal.

Labelling

The generic name is nylon or polyamide and there are a number of brand names including Bayer-Perlon®, Tactel® and Enka-Perlon®.

Aramid

Aramid and other **aromatic** polyamide fibres such as Nomex have very high tensile strength. The fibres can be five times stronger than steel of the same weight. They also have a high melting point which is followed by charring rather than the dripping characteristic of some other synthetic fibres. They will catch fire, they are combustible, but self-extinguish when removed from the source of heat. This gives them a high

■ A Grand Prix mechanic saved by his suit

resistance to fire. This is particularly important for garments such as suits for racing drivers. The fibres are also used in a wide range of industrial situations such as conveyer belts, foundry gloves, high-pressure hoses and heat-resistant cladding tiles on space vehicles.

Acrylic

A compound derived from oil called acrylonitrile is used to make the acrylic polymer. The acrylic polymer cannot be melt-spun to produce fibre because it decomposes when heated, so instead it is dissolved in chemicals and either wet-spun or dry-spun.

Labelling

The generic name is acrylic. To be allowed to be labelled acrylic, the actual fibres must have been made from at least 85 per cent acrylonitrile. Brand names include Courtelle® and Dralon®.

Elastane

Elastane is made from segmented polyurethane. It consists of rigid (stiff, firm) segments and flexible (soft, bendy) segments and it is this structure which gives elastane the built-in capacity to stretch and recover. The diagram shows the fibre without tension, under tension, and recovering from being under tension. Elastane is most usually used in a blend with other fibres because of its capacity to stretch and recover.

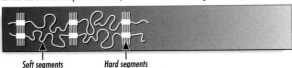
In the fibre's naturally relaxed state, the soft chains lie in tangled disorder.
Soft segments   Hard segments

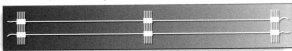
Under tension, the chains straighten out...

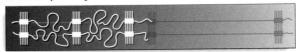
...while always straining to draw back to their natural tangle.

■ Elastane without tension, under tension and recovering from tension

Labelling

The generic name is elastane (known as spandex in the USA and Canada) and there are several brand names including Lycra® (made by DuPont).

DuPont state, 'The type of fabric and its end-use determine the amount and kind of Lycra® that will ensure optimum (the best) performance and aesthetic characteristics. As little as two per cent of Lycra® is enough to improve fabric quality, contributing liveliness, drape and better shape retention. Where body-hugging fit and high-performance stretch are required, as in swimwear, foundation garments or active sportswear, fabrics can contain from fourteen to forty per cent of Lycra®.'

— Task

a Carry out research into the use of elastane-type fibre in garments. Note the type of garments which have elastane in the fabric they are made from.
b Do they all contain the same amount?
c Look at the three claims made for Lycra®. Identify a garment for each claim which illustrates the description.

Better drape and fluidity
Fluid shapes have a new flow; unstructured silhouettes retain their form. LYCRA® improves both the hand and appearance of everything it touches, expands styling possibilities.

Improved shape retention
Garments with LYCRA® resist bagging and shed wrinkles. They keep their original shape and appearance through repeated laundering or dry cleaning.

More comfort and freedom
LYCRA® liberates even the most tailored clothes, enabling them to fit better and respond freely to every body movement. It contributes lasting qualities of flexibility, elasticity and recovery to fabrics and garments.

■ Claims made for Lycra®

49

Regenerated fibres

Viscose

Properties of viscose	
Strength	A very strong fibre (has a lower strength than cotton). Strength when wet is lower than for dry fibre (40–70 per cent only of dry strength).
Extensibility	Reasonably high breaking strength (15–30 per cent, which is twice that of cotton).
Elasticity	Does not recover well from stretching. (This means that viscose does not produce crease-resistant fabric.)
Static build-up	Low incidence because fibre always contains some moisture.
Handle and fineness	Depends on fineness of fibre produced and fabric construction. (Soft fine fabrics as well as firm fabrics can be produced.)
Dyeing	Fibres take dye very well and can be printed easily.
Lustre (shine/gloss)	Depends on the cross-section of the fibre and any chemicals which have been used to reduce lustre. Matt through to high lustre can be produced.
Thermal insulation	Generally viscose yarns do not have high insulation properties. Filament fibres have a low volume of trapped air within them which gives them a low capacity to insulate. Some staple fibre viscose yarns can be manufactured with a higher volume. This enhances the property to insulate.
Moisture – water absorption	In normal conditions 11–14 per cent of water vapour is absorbed. In liquid viscose swells and can absorb 80–120 per cent water.

Improvement of properties

When viscose fibres swell in water they thicken and this causes shrinkage in viscose fabrics. To help reduce this, synthetic resins are used to reduce moisture absorbency.

| Washing | Chlorine | Ironing | Dry cleaning | Drying |

Properties of synthetic fibres

Aftercare	
Polyester	**Polyamide**
Machine washable Quick drying Iron with care	Machine washable Quick drying

— Task —

Design a leaflet containing information to help consumers tell the difference between polyamide and polyester.

Properties of polyester and polyamide	Polyester	Polyamide
Strength	High tensile strength, wet strength same as dry.	Very strong. Stronger wet than dry (80–90 per cent stronger).
Extensibility	Breaking extension 15–50 per cent.	High breaking extensions whether dry or wet (useful for making rope etc.).
Elasticity	High degree of elasticity and resilience (makes it crease-resistant).	High degree of elasticity and resilience (therefore crease-resistant).
Static build-up	Very high degree of static build-up. (Anti-static treatments can reduce this.)	Very high degree of static build-up. (Anti-static treatments can reduce this.)
Fineness, handle	Can be produced to fit requirements.	Fabric construction, finishing and size of fibres (e.g. from micro to coarse) can be engineered into fibre production.
Lustre	Depends on cross-section of the fibre and any finishing techniques used. Can be made matt through to high lustre, according to needs of the end-product.	As for polyester.
Resistance to light, chemicals, heat	Very good resistance to light (therefore low potential to fade); mildew-proof, resistant to chemicals, heat, etc.	Resistant to alkalis and many solvents but attacked by strong acids.
Thermal insulation	Can be produced to increase insulating properties as required. Depends on type of fibre and yarn, whether filament staple or textured, etc.	Depends on fibre type. Textured filaments allow more air to be trapped, thus increasing the degree of insulation. Flat filament fibres trap little air and give a low degree of insulation.
Moisture absorption	Very low capacity to absorb moisture but can transport water in yarn by capillary action.	As for polyester.

2.14 Blending fibres

Why blend fibres?

The properties of one fibre can be improved by **blending** it with another fibre that has the properties the first one lacks. Blending takes place to:
- improve quality
- enhance appearance
- increase profitability.

Improvement of quality can be in:
- performance in use e.g. durability, abrasion, resistance, creasing, drape
- comfort e.g. moisture absorption, thermal insulation, feel
- ease of care e.g. laundering, drying, ironing, shrinking etc.

Appearance can be enhanced by:
- adding colour
- lustre
- producing fancy yarn.

Profitability can be increased by:
- controlling fibre cost and supply
- yarn count and uniformity (i.e. the fineness and same shape and size of the yarn)
- efficiency of manufacturing process.

When does blending take place?

Blending takes place during:
- staple yarn production by blending different types of fibres
- fabric production by mixing yarns from different fibres.

Which fibres are used?

Some blends are made with a mix of natural fibres and manufactured fibres, where the desirable properties of one counteract the disadvantages of the other. For example a good all-round performance is achieved when the comfort and insulating properties of natural fibres are blended with manufactured fibres and their properties of high strength, good abrasion resilience and easy-care characteristics.

Most cellulose and synthetic manufactured fibres are ideal for blending because they can be produced in the length and fineness required for particular end-uses.

Popular blends

Some of the most popular fabrics are blends of polyester and other fibres, for example polyester/cotton and polyester/viscose. These are examples of where the blend improves the quality of performance, comfort, ease of use and sometimes the appearance of a fabric. A blend of wool/viscose is almost always produced in order to reduce price and/or increase profitability.

How much of each fibre?

The percentage of each fibre in the blend gives an indication of the properties of the fabric. For example there must be enough of each fibre to give the blend the beneficial qualities of each. Blending is a compromise between the properties of two different fibres. No single fibre has an ideal set of properties. If a blend of polyester and cotton is taken as an example, cotton has a high water absorbency property and a low degree of static build-up, and polyester is very durable, has good shape retention and is quick drying. Combining these fibres produce a fabric which possesses the best properties from both cotton and polyester.

Task

a Identify *two* different blended fabrics (use fabrics in the piece or products).
b List the proportions used in each fabric.
c Explain why blends are used in products such as bed linen, school trousers and sportswear.

*T*extiles are 'finished' to improve their functional qualities. For example this could be:
➤ to enhance their appearance by colouring
➤ embossing
➤ to change the texture, draping qualities and 'feel' of a fabric
➤ to modify wearing qualities (such as creasing, flammability, durability, water-proofing and water-repellence etc.) or
➤ to modify care requirements (e.g. shrinkage control, **colourfastness** etc.).

Finishing can enhance the aesthetic appeal of fabrics as well as giving them enhanced safety, protection and durability properties.

Changing texture

The texture of a fabric can be changed by **calendering**. In this process a fabric is passed between heated rollers under pressure. Various effects can be produced dependent on the nature of the roller surfaces for example:
➤ Using high-speed metal rollers and applying a synthetic resin produces a glazed finish (glazed Chintz is an example).
➤ Two layers of a ribbed fabric calendered slightly 'off grain' produce a Moiré effect. (Moiré is a type of watermark pattern.)
➤ Rollers with a raised design emboss the fabric i.e. produce a relief pattern. With synthetic fibres the heated rollers produce a more permanent effect.

Changing handling qualities

The handle (draping qualities and feel) of a fabric can be temporarily changed by:
➤ **sizing (or dressing)** This gives body, weight and lustre to fabrics by stiffening them with glue, clay or wax. These stiffenings wash out during laundering and may leave the fabric limp and susceptible to wear.
➤ **weighting** This is a process applied to silk. Metallic salts are absorbed to produce a heavier fabric.

Other finishes

Aspects of performance can be improved by applying finishes so that the resulting fabric better meets consumer expectations. These include:
➤ **anti-bacterial finishes** These check the growth and the effect of bacteria and perspiration.
➤ **anti-static finishes** These reduce 'clinging' by dispersing static electricity.
➤ **flame-resistant finishes** These prevent the spread of flame once the source has been removed or extinguished, or make the textile difficult to ignite or non-flammable (flame-retardant fibres are self-extinguishing to a great extent).
➤ **mercerization** This is a process in which caustic soda solution is used to treat cotton yarn or fabric. The effect is that the cross-section of the fibre swells, making stronger and more lustrous yarns and fabrics. This process also allows the yarns and fabrics to be dyed or printed more effectively (i.e. a deeper shade for a given amount of colour).
➤ **easy-care properties** The application of chemicals (e.g. resins) reduces the sensitivity of a fibre to moisture and creasing and fabrics become crease-resistant, quick-drying and resistant to shrinking.
➤ **stain resistance** The fabric is treated with silicones which help prevent water-borne stains and/or synthetic resins which help prevent oil-borne stains.
➤ **anti-pilling** Film forming polymers or solvents can be applied to reduce the incidence of tiny fibre pills appearing on the surface of fabrics made from both wool and synthetic fibres.

Task

Investigate how the aesthetic appeal of fabrics is improved by finishing. Find examples of garments and household textiles which benefit from this.

Record your findings in your notebook.

2.16 *Textured yarns*

*T*he properties of flat, continuous filament yarns can be altered by texturing processes.

What does texturing do?

Texturing:
- ➤ increases the volume of the yarn
- ➤ reduces lustre
- ➤ allows more air to be trapped, thus increasing the degree of thermal insulation offered
- ➤ increases vapour permeability and transport of moisture
- ➤ makes softer fabrics
- ➤ increases elasticity and extensibility.

Types of textured yarns

- ➤ **Stretch yarns** These are highly elastic (with an extension of 150–300 per cent).
- ➤ **Stabilized yarns** These are subjected to setting treatments which reduce their elasticity.
- ➤ **Bulked yarns** These are yarns which have been made bigger whilst maintaining normal elasticity and extensibility properties.
- ➤ **High-bulked yarns** These are usually made by blending fibres i.e. those with a high tendency to shrink and those with a low tendency to shrink. The fibres are then heated. This causes the fibres with a high tendency to shrink to contract, which in turn makes the fibres with a low tendency to shrink crumple.

Brushing

This is sometimes called **raising**. In this process the fibre ends of a fabric are brushed out by being passed over a series of rollers which are covered with wire. The wire-clad rollers hook into the surface of the fabric as it passes over them. When flat-filament nylon which has been warp-knitted is treated in this way, brushed nylon is produced. A fluffy surface and a soft handle are produced when fabrics are brushed. The process thickens the fabric and increases the amount of air which can be trapped, which creates the warm effect.

Trevira® fleece is a development by Hoechst, a German fibre-producing company. It is claimed that Trevira® fleece contains 95 per cent air in a lightweight fibre, which makes it an excellent insulator suitable for winter and summer use. The photos show examples of its uses.

■ Clothes made from Trevira® fleece

― Task ―

The manufacturer of a brushed cotton fabric has asked you to help design products which use this fabric.

a Suggest *two* different products which you think will be popular with the consumer.

b Produce a design sheet which shows the colour ranges of one of the products.

c **Annotate** (label) the design sheet to show why your suggestions will be popular and are likely to sell well.

The first step in making fabric is the production of yarn from fibres. Various methods of spinning are used to do this. Spinning systems used for different types of fibre are summarized in the table on the right.

The production of yarns

Yarns are single strands, i.e. they are one-dimensional. In order to manufacture fabric from yarns the single strands must be combined so that the structure becomes two-dimensional. This is achieved in both weaving and knitting but, before either of these procedures takes place, yarns can be processed to produce the particular properties required in the final fabric.

Twist

Particular properties in the yarn can be achieved by applying different amounts of twist to bind fibres together. For example, a small amount of twist will give a soft yarn but as the amount of twist is increased the softness decreases. This can be useful, for example, when considering drape. A yarn with a high amount of twist will produce a fabric which does not drape well and therefore would not be suitable for making curtains or anything which requires good draping quality. Twist can be put into a yarn:

➤ clockwise where the fibres twist to the right
➤ anti-clockwise where the fibres twist to the left.

Clockwise twist corresponds to the shape of the letter S and is called S-twist. Anti-clockwise twist corresponds to the shape of the letter Z and is called Z-twist. The diagram illustrates the two twists.

Spinning systems for different types of fibre		
Fibre	**Spinning system**	**Fibre length**
Long staple e.g. wool, some manufactured fibres	Woollen system Worsted system	18–60 mm 60–120 mm
Short staple e.g. cotton, some manufactured fibres	Condenser system (similar to woollen system)	10–25 mm
	Cotton system (ring spinning)	20–50 mm
	Rotor spinning	10–100 mm
Silk	Spun silk Noil silk	up to 250 mm up to 60 mm
Manufactured fibres	Converter Direct spinning	continuous

Types of yarn

The usual methods of spinning produce single yarns that can be processed to give different properties. For example, to make a yarn thicker or stronger, two or more single yarns may be twisted together. Single yarns twisted together in this way make a **plied yarn**. Two single yarns twisted together are called two-ply, four singles twisted together are called four-ply etc. Plied yarns are stronger and can withstand the pressures exerted on them during weaving better than single yarns which tend to fray. The diagram below shows three types of plied yarns.

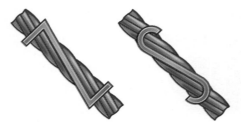

■ S-twist and Z-twist

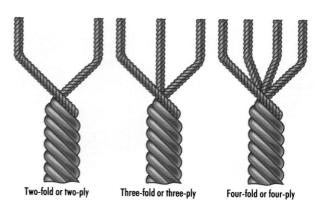

Two-fold or two-ply   Three-fold or three-ply   Four-fold or four-ply

■ Plied yarns

Fancy yarns

In addition to increasing the strength of a yarn, plying makes it possible to produce a variety of yarns, e.g. fancy yarns. These can be produced in several ways, for example by blending fibres of different colours and spinning them as one yarn, by printing or dyeing a pattern on to the sliver and so on. Other methods of producing fancy yarns include twisting together two or more yarns which are different in some way, e.g. colour, softness, thickness etc. The amount and direction of twist may be altered to produce an uneven effect. However the effect is achieved, fancy yarns give colour and texture and can be very decorative. Every fancy yarn has a specific name which identifies how it was produced, the fibres from which it was made and its appearance.

Most fancy yarns are based on two or more plies, with one ply being the core, another ply giving the special effect and an additional third ply which holds the other two together. Examples include:

➤ **spiral yarn** This is a two-ply yarn twisted with another yarn which is thick, soft and twisted.
➤ **gimp yarn** This is very like spiral yarn but is harder and finer. It has two fine yarns twisting in opposite directions, holding a third thread in position to make an S-loop. It is easy to recognize because it is in the shape of the letter S.

➤ **knop yarn** In this case two yarns are twisted together, with one of them being wound round and round the other to form a lump or **knop**. These two yarns are then twisted in the opposite direction with a third yarn which binds them together. This yarn has knots at intervals along the yarn.
➤ **bouclé yarn** This name refers to yarns which have a knot, loop or curl effect. These yarns are made with two or more yarns twisted together. The loops stick out from the main part of the yarn.

— Tasks

1 a Identify fabrics made from each of the fancy yarns described above.
  b Describe the qualities each of these give to the fabric and/or the product made with the fabric. Record these in your notebook. If possible include annotated swatches.
2 Find samples of a knop yarn and a bouclé yarn. In addition you will need a hand lens and a dissecting needle.
  a Examine each yarn, using the hand lens.
  b Separate the plies of each sample using the dissecting needle. In each case, identify which is the core ply and which is the ply that gives the effect.
  c Record your findings in your notebook.

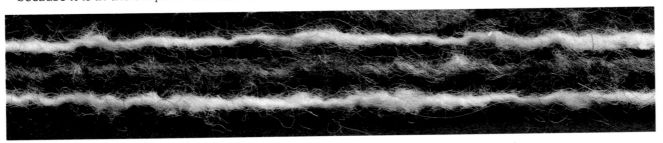

■ Knop yarn

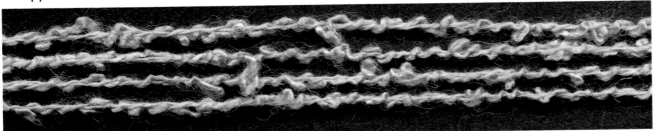

■ Bouclé yarn

*I*n the three basic processes, fabric is produced from:

- ➤ fibres – fabrics which are non woven e.g. felted, bonded
- ➤ yarns – fabrics which are woven, knitted, braided, open-work fabrics
- ➤ a combination of fibres – fabrics which are **laminated**.

Non-woven fabrics

The process of yarn production is missed out for these fabrics and, instead, webs of fibre are produced which are sometimes called batts. The webs of fibre are bonded together either mechanically or chemically. After the web formation, non-woven fabrics are produced by one of the following methods: needle punching; stitch bonding; thermal bonding; or adhesive bonding. They are strengthened by stitching or by application of adhesives or chemicals which dissolve or melt small areas of the fibres. These are sometimes called **bonded-fibre** fabrics. Compared with other fabrics, they are stiffer, less flexible and drape less well; they have virtually no elasticity. They are not very durable but are very popular for making disposable garments and articles such as J cloths. Vilene is one example of a non-woven fabric.

Fabrics from yarns

- ➤ **Woven fabrics** are made by interlacing two sets of yarns at right angles to each other.
- ➤ **Knits** are made by interlocking loops of yarn. There are **weft-knitted** fabrics where the yarns go across the fabric width; there are also **warp-knitted** fabrics where the yarns go down the length of the fabric.
- ➤ **Open-work fabrics** include lace and nets.
- ➤ **Braided fabrics** are made by interleaving at least three yarns in a diagonal pattern.

Laminated fabrics

These are made by sticking two or more fabrics together or by sticking/bonding fabrics to foam, film or paper.

The photos show the types of fabrics produced by each process.

Tasks

1 Examine some of the items of clothing you are wearing. Identify a woven fabric and a knitted fabric.
2 Look for an example of a non-woven fabric. Where would you expect to find it? Why is it used in that situation?

Knitted fabric

Braided fabric

Woven fabric

Open work fabric

Needle felt fabric

Laminated fabric

■ The fabrics produced by the processes above

Non-woven fabrics are produced by combining fibres in various ways. Felt is a particular type of non-woven fabric.

Felt has exciting possibilities for use but what is it? It is made using the tendency of some fibres, particularly wool, to change their character when moisture, warmth and pressure are applied. Taking wool as an example, this is what happens in very simple terms. When wool is subjected to water, heat and agitation (vigorous movement), as in washing, the fibres move and slip over each other. At the same time, the interlocking scales of each fibre hook into each other, causing a reduction in size and a change in appearance. A matted structure is produced and the fibres 'felt' as a result. In the case of a garment shrinkage results.

Producing felt commercially

Felt can be produced from wool or from some other animal fibres, such as goat, rabbit or camel hair. The fibres are laid over each other in layers until the desired thickness, width and length are achieved. This produces a web-type structure which is then beaten, pressed and squeezed until the required degree of felting is reached. The felt can be strengthened by stitching, by melting or dissolving small areas of fibres, or by gluing with adhesives.

Another type of felt is called **needle felt**. This can be produced using almost any type of fibre. Synthetic fibres are increasingly used for this commercially. This method uses felting needles which are arranged together in a needling machine. Fibre webs are layered on top of each other and are fed into the needling machine. The needles are pushed through the fibre webs in order to drag a number of fibres to the bottom layer of the webs. This makes loops in the fibres which stitch the webs together.

Properties of felt

All felts absorb water and are good insulators. Felt can be steamed and pressed and formed into permanent shapes. This means that felt can be used in many different ways. Commercial uses include hats, billiard table coverings, insulation materials, collar facings for coats and jackets.

Needle felts have the additional property of being elastic and lightweight compared with other non-woven fabrics. Their uses include interlinings, mattress covers, upholstery materials and wadding.

Case study: The use of felt

Annie Sherburne, one of the designer-makers featured in Unit 5 (see page 117) finds felt a perfect medium for designing and making. Annie says that ideas which are the starting point of any design spring from all sorts of places. When using felt to implement a design-and-make product she is inspired by a particular material. If she likes the material she takes ideas directly from it, as with some fluffy fleece with which she experimented. The outcome was the production of her own felt which she used to make the outfit shown in the photo.

■ Annie and the felt she made

■ Annie wearing the outfit

Task

Examine a sample/swatch of felt by feeling it and looking at it, using a hand lens. Record your findings.

3.4 Weaving

Weaving is one of the processes which uses yarns to produce a two-dimensional fabric. The yarns are interlaced at right angles to each other during the weaving process. The yarns which run lengthwise in a fabric are called the warp and the yarns which go across the width of a fabric are called the weft. The warp yarns are known as **ends**. The weft yarns are known as **picks**. The diagram on the right shows the method very simply. A simple loom is shown where the weft yarn moves alternately under and then over the warp. This produces a plain weave.

How weaving works

The loom is threaded (set up) with the warp yarns. For the first row the weft yarn is woven *over* the first warp thread and *under* the next warp thread, and so on. For the next row the weft is woven *under* the first warp thread and *over* the next warp thread, and so on. The weaving continues in this way, alternating the under and over actions as described. A shuttle is used to do this (see page 8).

Groups of warp threads are lifted up and down by a frame called a **heddle** or **heald**, which is labelled in the diagram of the weaving process, on page 59. The diagram below shows a plain weave.

The warp yarns are fed from the warp beam to the breast beam. The **heddle shafts** lift them up according to the pattern required. The reed holds the lifted yarn in place and the shuttle threads the weft yarns through to produce the woven fabric. This is wound onto the cloth beam. The diagram at the top of page 59 shows the complete process.

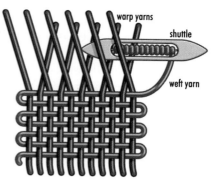

■ A simple loom

In order to give a fabric a good edge, double or stronger yarns are placed in the warp at both ends. These form the **selvedge** which gives a firmness to the edges of the fabric. Variations in weave can be achieved in a number of ways, such as using different colours and weights of yarns, altering the weave etc.

Designing weaves

A designer needs to be able to present a particular design weave in diagrammatic form, to specify how it will be achieved. This involves making a specification of the different colours or textures of yarns to be used, and the sequence in which they will be used. British Standard BS2861 specifies

	Interlacings
Plain weave Each warp yarn is lifted over alternate weft yarns.	
Twill weave This construction makes a pattern of diagonal lines. Each warp yarn lifts over (and/or remains under) more than one weft.	
Satin weave The warp floats over four or more wefts and remains under only one. Adjacent warps arranged are as randomly as possible, so no twill line is made.	

■ Some basic weaves

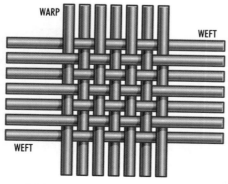

■ Plain weave fabric

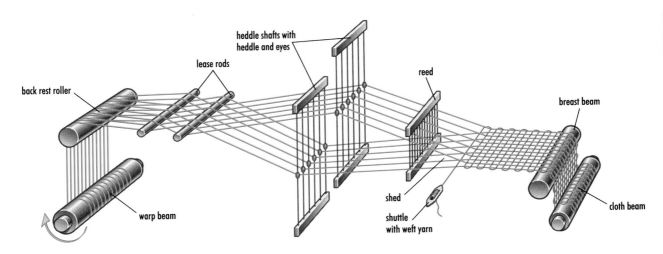

■ The weaving process

types of weave diagrams which are understood by designers and weavers all over the world. The three diagrams on the right show this.

The three diagrams below show different weave patterns. They show the cloth construction required and are called pattern drafts.

The generic names of some fabrics are derived partly from the weave pattern used and partly from the fibre from which they are made. For example, muslin, percale, cheesecloth and lawn are all plain weaves, whereas gabardine is a type of twill weave (a twill weave is made when weft threads cross the warp threads at different intervals to produce a diagonal effect).

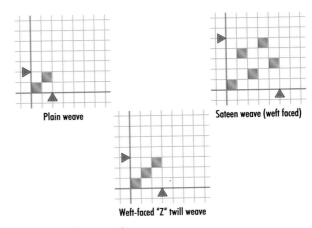

Plain weave

Sateen weave (weft faced)

Weft-faced "Z" twill weave

■ BS2861 specifies weave diagrams

━ *Task*

a Collect a sample/swatch of:
   a plain woven fabric
   a twill weave fabric
   a satin weave fabric.
b Mount them in your notebook. Label them.
c Describe the qualities of each sample. Include reference to the fibres from which they are made.

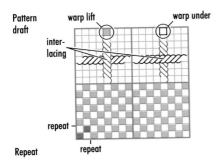

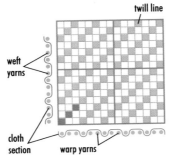

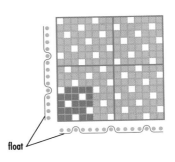

■ A designer is able to develop fabrics with a range of colourways using weave diagrams (such as these). This can now be done on a computer using special programs.

3.5 Different types of loom

The Jacquard loom

Jacquard weaving was invented by a French silk weaver called Joseph-Marie Jacquard, after whom the system is named. In this system each individual warp can be lifted in a pre-planned sequence to produce a particular design on the fabric. The weave design is applied to cards in the sequence (order) in which it should appear on the fabric. The sequence is punched into cards which move on a type of belt. The cards control individual cords which are weighted at the bottom and through which the warp yarns are threaded. The cords lift the warp yarns in the sequence punched into the cards (see the diagrams). The cards are suspended above the cords.

— Task

1 a Identify some fabrics which have been woven by this method.
   b Collect samples/swatches if possible. Mount and label them in your notebook.
   c Describe the designs which have been produced on the fabrics.

The Dobby loom

This type of loom is used to produce mechanically simple weaves and limited designs very quickly. The loom can carry up to 32 shafts, but usually only 4–16 are used. The way each individual warp end is put through the healds depends upon the design required. The shaft selection is controlled by the dobby mechanism and each shaft is raised in sequence according to the peg plan. The pegs are joined together to form a **lag** and the peg plan creates the design. Each lag is one pick of the weave. A large number of lags may be used and these are joined together to make a continuous chain. Fabrics woven on the Dobby loom include Bedford cord (corduroy). The weave is usually plain or twill. The distinctive appearance of cord is produced by stripes which look like ridges. The ridges stick up because the spaces between them are deep furrows (i.e. hollows between the ridges).

Pique is another example of a fabric produced on a Dobby loom. It has an embossed, quilted appearance. This texture is formed by a series of raised and hollow parts of the cloth, which form the design. Various types of pique are available and they are usually made from cotton yarns. Generally, pique fabric has good wearing and washing properties and also keeps its shape well. Fine pique is used for dress fabrics and other light apparel. Pique that is woven with thicker yarns is suitable for upholstery.

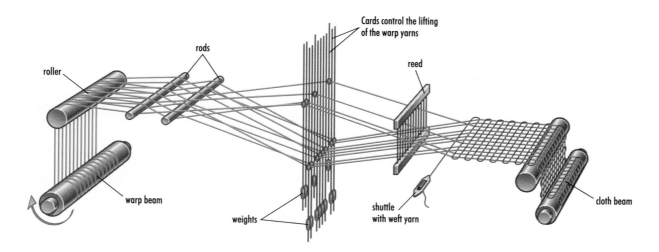

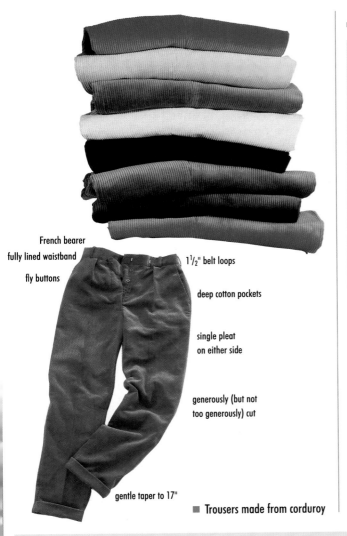

French bearer
fully lined waistband
fly buttons
$1\frac{1}{2}$" belt loops
deep cotton pockets
single pleat
on either side
generously (but not
too generously) cut
gentle taper to 17"

■ Trousers made from corduroy

Tasks

2   Collect a sample of Bedford cord fabric. Examine the ridges and hollows for size, separation (distance between them) and texture. Mount the sample in your notebook and include the results of your examination.

3   Collect a sample of pique fabric. Examine it to discover how the raised and hollow parts have been used to create a design. Describe the feel of the sample. Mount the sample in your notebook and include the results of your examination.

4   A craft-shop owner has asked you to suggest a product line which could be displayed in the shop to show the use of a particular type of woven fabric. Produce a story-board which shows:
    a   your product idea in detail
    b   swatches of the fabric you have chosen
    c   a flow diagram showing the main steps in the making of the product.

New developments in technology

Case study: Computer technology in the design of fabrics and in weaving

Scot Innovation and Development Ltd has developed a **computer-aided design** (CAD) package which can create designs in a matter of hours rather than days, at a fraction of the cost of previous systems. This design system is called ScotWeave.

The traditional design process in weaving has not changed much since the first loom was invented. The invention of the Jacquard loom made it possible to produce more complicated designs but punching the cards for a design takes a long time. Each time the shuttle crosses the loom a separate

(continued on next page)

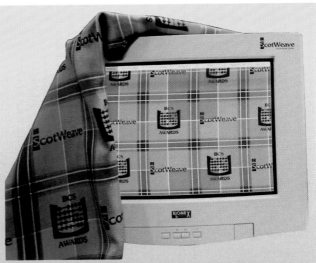

■ The Scotweave computer-aided design program

61

punched card is needed for each yarn; thousands of cards are needed for a complex design (e.g. there are often 100 yarns to every 2.5 cm on a loom 30 cm across).

Designers of a pattern seldom knew exactly what the finished product would look like. From the development of the original design to the production of the woven fabric could take up to six months.

ScotWeave is a complete CAD package which can produce all types of design in any material, e.g. multi-section blankets, complex weave structures and **kaleidoscopic** patterns. Design and colour measurements can be made on screen. Sixteen million colours can be defined and shown on screen. Scot Innovation and Development started when, in 1980, a lecturer in weaving taught himself to program a computer as part of a research project. His aim was to use computer graphics to develop a unique design

tool for traditional Scottish fabrics. Scot Innovation and Design is a **subsidiary** of the Scottish College of Textiles, but it is totally separate because the college has charitable status. ScotWeave recently won a John Logie Baird award for innovation. ScotWeave is a professional tool for industry, using the latest technology to help designers visualize their work, reduce design times and, where possible, directly control modern electronic production equipment. The control and direction of this development has always been in the hands of modern textiles experts. The program follows the traditional design process as closely as possible and a minimum of training is required to use it. It can be used for both Jacquard and Dobby weaving.

The system has largely eliminated the need for fabric samples because designs can be printed on paper (see the examples of the paper printouts illustrated).

■ Examples of fabrics produced using the ScotWeave program

3.6 Knitted fabrics

Knitted fabrics are made from interlocking loops, using one or more yarns. The knit construction is based on a continuous yarn arranged with interlocking loops. (The yarn lies both horizontally and vertically and interlocking them produces a two-dimensional form.) The two types are **weft-knitted** and **warp-knitted**.

Weft-knitted fabrics

- A single yarn may be used.
- The fabric is made by forming the loops of yarn across the width or around in a circle.
- This can become unravelled and form a ladder.

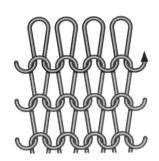

Warp-knitted fabrics

- The yarn loops are formed in a vertical direction, the fabric is held together by the interlocking of these vertical loops with the loops on alternate sides.
- The fabric does not become unravelled and therefore does not ladder.

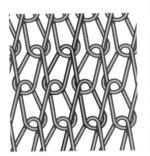

Type of fabrics produced

Weft knits

These are produced in industry on circular knitting machines which are capable of producing a lot of fabric reasonably quickly. This makes the process very **cost-effective**. Single and double jersey fabrics, interlock fabrics and hosiery are made by this method. In addition weft knits can be flat-bed or fully fashioned.

Warp knits

Several yarns are used in warp knitting. These are wound parallel to each other on a warp beam and fed into the knitting machine where they form lengthwise loops. This is one of the fastest methods of producing fabric. The needles used vary according to the type of fabric being produced. Tricot is one example (the name comes from the French *tricoter*, meaning to 'knit'). Tricot has good permeability and drape properties and is comfortable to wear. It is resistant to both running and fraying. Raschel is another example.

These knits are becoming very popular because they can be produced in a wide variety of fabrics, ranging from soft, fine and net-type through to coarser structures. They are characterized by a chain of fine yarn which holds a heavier, textured yarn in a lacy, open structure.

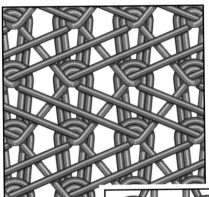

■ A tricot knit

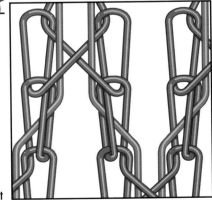

■ A raschel knit

— Tasks —

1 Identify fabrics which are:
   a weft-knitted   b tricot knits   c raschel knits.
   Collect samples of each (or photographs of products if samples are unavailable).
2 Mount and label them in your notebook.

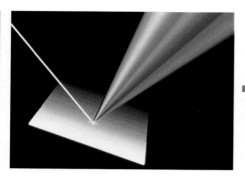

■ Computer artwork showing white light being split into the spectrum of colours

*C*olour is an important consideration when choosing textiles and textile items. The colour of an article is almost always the first attribute used to describe it. The principle of applying colour to textiles is based on the fact that visible light can be divided into coloured lights, called the **spectrum**. These colours are: red, orange, yellow, green, blue, indigo and violet. They are seen in a rainbow.

When white light falls on an object certain colours of the spectrum are absorbed; the colours which can be seen are reflected. White objects reflect all the colours in the spectrum of white light, and taken together these produce white. Black objects absorb all the colours of the spectrum of white light so that none is reflected, hence they look black. A red object reflects only red light, and absorbs all the other colours in white light (see the diagram). Dyes applied to textiles cause some colours of the spectrum to be absorbed and others to be reflected.

Colour schemes

When designing for manufacture, planning colour schemes is an important part of textiles technology.

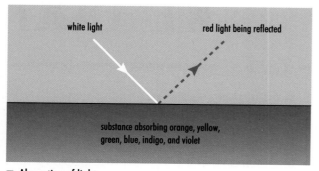

white light   red light being reflected

substance absorbing orange, yellow, green, blue, indigo, and violet

It is also an important aspect of design-and-make tasks in school. Colour schemes must appeal to the target market. In the diagram, the colour wheel shows primary and secondary colours. This is helpful when planning colour combinations.

Primary and secondary colours

There are many different colour combinations which form the basis of colour schemes. The main ones are:

- **monochromatic** Different intensities (depth) of one colour are used in the scheme or maybe black and white only are used.
- **complementary** Colours which are directly opposite each other on the colour wheel are used. Examples would be red and green, and blue and orange.
- **analogous (similar or parallel)** Colours which are very close to each other on the colour wheel are used together. Examples would be blue, blue-green and green.

The effects of colour

Colours affect the way people feel; their moods can vary according to the colour scheme of their surroundings. For example:

- monochromatic schemes can be monotonous but they also give a very neat, ordered effect

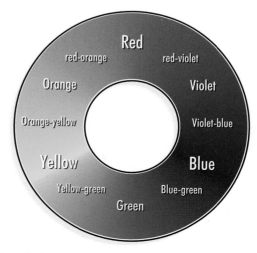

Red
red-orange   red-violet
Orange   Violet
Orange-yellow   Violet-blue
Yellow   Blue
Yellow-green   Blue-green
Green

■ Absorption of light

■ A colour wheel

➤ analogous schemes can create restful, comfortable sensations
➤ complementary schemes can be very exciting and different, if direct opposite colours are used they are a strong, bold combination.

— *Task* —

1 Look at the colour schemes used in the photos. Describe the effect or mood which each suggests.

More details about colour

It is important to understand that where there is no light there is no colour. Look at the colour wheel shown opposite. There are twelve colours. Notice:
➤ the three **primary** colours, yellow, red and blue
➤ the **secondary** colours, orange, green and violet
➤ the **tertiary** colours, yellow-green, blue-green, blue-violet, red-violet, red-orange, yellow-orange.

It is possible to make many more than these twelve colours by mixing together different colours according to the effect required. To do this successfully the following terms which are used to describe colours should be understood.
➤ **Hue** This is the name of the colour e.g. blue, yellow-green.
➤ **Value** This is the lightness or darkness of a colour and describes how near it is to black or white. Light colour tones are called tints, dark colour tones are called shades (e.g. pink is a tint of red, navy is a shade of blue).
➤ **Intensity** This is the degree of brilliance, dullness or greyness in a colour i.e. its strength.

How is an understanding of colours used in designing with textiles?

Modern consumers demand that textiles are attractive, colourful and resistant to spoilage by wear, sunlight and modern laundering systems. The colours and designs demanded are produced by dyeing and printing fibres, yarns and fabrics using a variety of methods which fulfil those demands.

Whatever the method used the consumer expects the colour to be permanent i.e. colourfast.

■ Colours and their effects

— *Task* —

2 A manufacturer of beachwear has asked you to suggest *two* different colour schemes for use by the designer of the new season's collection.
a Using your understanding of colour combinations and the effects they can create, show, with coloured illustrations, the two schemes you suggest.
b Explain the effects which each of your suggested schemes will create.
c Present your work in a form suitable to show to the manufacturer.

3.8 Dyeing and printing

*F*rom the earliest of times, people have wanted coloured textiles. For thousands of years natural pigments have been used to produce dyes. These include vegetable pigments which produce, for example, indigo and saffron colours and mineral pigments which produce red and yellow ochre.

Dyeing

In industry dyes are often referred to as **dyestuffs**. Dyes are added during processing. Most modern dyes are synthetically manufactured to imitate natural products. Successful dyeing depends on the extent to which the dyestuff will bond to the fabric (or yarn) and remain fast. This is not as easy as it may sound because dyes and fibres are made of different chemicals. This means that the bonding which is required may not take place because the dyestuff and fibre may not combine successfully, i.e. there is no **affinity** between the two. It is essential that the right dyestuff is chosen for a particular fibre or fabric. Another problem arises in dyeing two different fabrics the same colour, as the two fabrics may need different dyes to achieve the colour match.

The textile/dye colourist must be able to:
- achieve the right colour
- match colour on two (or more) different fabrics
- make sure the colours are fast (don't run or wash out)
- make sure the dye is applied evenly
- make sure the fabric is not damaged by the process.

Dyeing methods

Dye is almost always either dissolved or **suspended** in very small particles in water. The textile is then immersed (plunged) in it. The temperature of the dye solution and the time for which the textile is immersed depend upon the type of dye being used. Some dyes can work in cold water but most dyes need heat and a considerable amount of time to produce successful results. The methods and machines used commercially for dyeing vary according to the fibre type and whether fibre, yarn or fabric is being dyed. Not all fibre types take up dye readily. For example, cotton and polyester react differently to dyes. Some dyes are good with polyester but not with cotton and vice versa.

The processes

- **Batchwise process** A whole batch of textile material passes through a single process in a given amount of time. After this process the textile material usually has to undergo two additional processes; the first is **fixation** and the second is washing. Fixation is the fixing of the dye to make sure it is fast. This is carried out using steam which condenses on the textile; this transfers heat and helps the dyestuff to be diffused within the fibres. Washing removes excess dyes and chemicals.
- **Continuous process** The textile material passes through a sequenced series of processes where it is dyed, the colour is fixed and, if necessary, the textile is washed.

Technical terms associated with dyeing

- **Substrate** This is the fibre, yarn or fabric which is to be dyed.
- **Mordant** This is a substance which can create an affinity between a dyestuff and fibre. It also helps to improve colourfastness.
- **Disperse dyes** These are insoluble in water but when reduced to very small particles can be suspended of **dispersed** in water. Disperse dyes are used for some synthetic fibres such as polyester.
- **Vat dyeing** The dye used is insoluble in water but can be made soluble by the addition of a chemical called a **reducing agent**, which removes oxygen. The soluble dye produced is dissolved in water in a vat (a large tank) and the textile material is immersed in it so that the dye can diffuse or spread into the fibre. After dyeing the textile material is exposed to the air or treated with a chemical called an **oxidizing agent**, which gives it back its oxygen. The dyestuff becomes insoluble again and is, therefore, fast.

When can dyeing take place?

These are the various stages of manufacture at which dyeing can take place.

➤ **At the fibre stage, before they are spun into yarn** The dye is able to penetrate each fibre and gives a uniform colour and good colourfastness.

➤ **At the liquid polymer stage (in the case of manufactured fibres) before extrusion through the spinneret** The dye becomes part of the fibre and creates almost perfect colourfastness.

➤ **At the yarn stage** At this stage the dye penetrates very well but maybe not as uniformly as at the fibre stage.

➤ **At the fabric stage (sometimes called piece dyeing)** This is a cost-effective method since it allows manufacturers to store undyed fabric and to dye it according to demand. Cross-dyeing takes place at the fabric stage when a fabric is made from different fibres which have different affinities for the dyestuffs being used. This produces a number of different effects, for example, designs woven into the fabric take on various colours as in checks, plaids, and striped materials.

— Task

The photos show examples of dyeing.
a Identify a likely target market for each product shown.
b Choose one of the products and explain the effect dyeing it has created.

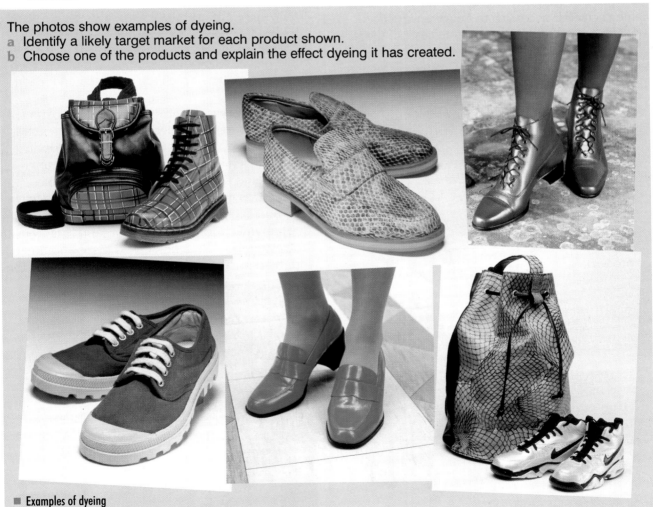

■ **Examples of dyeing**

*T*he following methods of applying colour can be used in design-and-make activities in school.

Tie-dyeing is a very ancient method of producing interesting and different colour effects. The fabric is folded, tied tightly at intervals with thread and then immersed in dye. The dye penetrates the fabric unevenly and creates a 'sunburst' effect. The blending of several colours and tying the fabric at different intervals produces unique and interesting colour effects. (Focused task sheets 5a–5c in the Teacher's Resource Pack explain this technique.)

Batik is another ancient method of applying colour to fabric. It involves the application of wax to the fabric, to act as a barrier between the fabric and the dye. It is called a **resist method** of dyeing, i.e. the wax resists the dye, so that the areas covered by it are not coloured. Interesting and different effects can be achieved according to how the wax is applied. A different effect can be achieved if the wax is cracked. The wax is boiled off after dyeing has taken place. (Focused task sheets 6a–6c in the Teacher's Resource Pack explain this technique.)

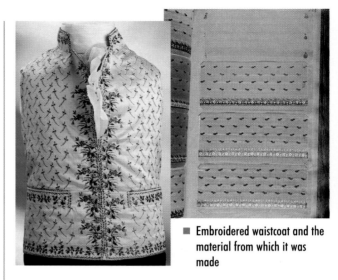

■ Embroidered waistcoat and the material from which it was made

The photos (left) show examples of colour and surface decoration that have been applied by tie-dyeing and batik. Tie-dyed and batik fabric can be used to produced unique products. In addition, pieces of fabric can be quilted, layered or used in whole pieces to produce exciting and different ideas for products which are designed and made in school.

Embroidery is a method of applying colour, shapes, textures and lines to fabric using stitches and threads of different kinds. It can be done by hand or machine. The photos above show an embroidered waistcoat and the material from which it was made. The waistcoat was made in 1789 and is on show at the Victoria and Albert Museum in London. The material sample is from the pattern book of a firm called Maze and Steer and the particular silk pattern it shows was for the

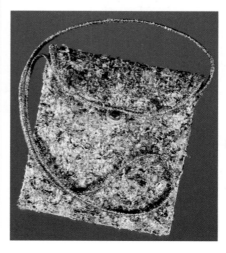

■ This machine-embroidered bag was made by a pupil of Beverley High School in a design-and-make task.

■ Tie-dye and batik (left centre)

winter collection of 1789. This type of pattern book is an early example of how designers and manufacturers show clients their ideas for particular collections.

Successful colour effects can be produced with hand or machine embroidery using:

➤ a detailed **graphic image** of the effect required (this can be a commercially produced transfer or a graphic image produced by a computer or free-hand)

➤ a **specification** showing; fabric(s) to be used, colour, stitching direction, stitch density (thickness) and stitch type details.

■ Poem 500 embroidery machine

Appliqué is a method of producing different colour and textural effects by layering fabrics of different colours, shapes and textures.

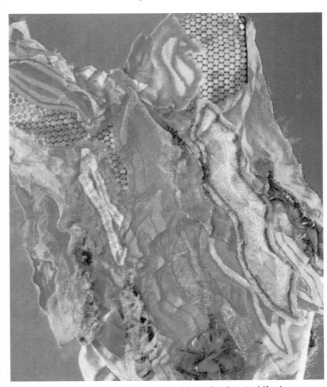

■ Appliqué done by a pupil at George Abbot School in Guildford

Task

A local textile museum is planning to open a gift shop which will stock a number of textile products. One of the themes that has been chosen for product development is 'Colour and Texture in Textile Products'. You have been invited to put together a collection of ideas for products to illustrate this theme. The museum wants to include a variety of textile products, all of which are suitable for selling in the gift shop. In your research you will need to consider:

➤ the type of people who are likely to visit a textile museum, for example age groups, interests etc.
➤ products which are popular with consumers in similar circumstances
➤ how easily your suggested products can be produced in quantity
➤ production costs
➤ selling price.

a Suggest suitable products for this purpose (remember that each product must sell well).
b Choose *one* of your suggestions. Make a sketch of it or model it using a computer if you can. Include details of the product and the type of consumer to whom you think it will appeal.
c Prepare a detailed list of equipment and materials that will be required to produce a sample of the product. Include details of how you are going to apply colour (or colour and texture).
d Present the work you have carried out to show to the curator of the museum. One way to do this is to use a story-board to communicate your ideas. This is a set of illustrated boards which show your ideas, in sequence, from initial suggestions through to sketches and details of the product you have chosen. The boards must be capable of being used without bending.

*P*rinting has been used for more than two thousand years. Small pieces of cloth which have been found in Egyptian tombs and the Pyramids are decorated with patterns, providing evidence of early printing. There are many printing techniques; some of them can be carried out in school and others can only be carried out successfully using commercial methods.

Techniques that can be used in school

Block printing, transfer, stencil and screen printing can be carried out in school very successfully to produce original designs for small quantities of fabrics. Painting fabrics can also produce original designs; however, this and the methods mentioned above are time-consuming and therefore may not meet time and cost criteria for product development. Care must be taken with all these techniques to make sure a professional finish can be achieved using the resources at hand and in the time available.

How do these methods work?

Block printing is the easiest method of printing. A design is cut into a flat surface by removing the background and leaving the design raised. Dye is applied to the block which is then pressed onto the fabric. Initial ideas of colour and shape can be tested out in this way, but only small areas of fabric can be covered at any one time and a different block is needed for every colour. In industry the method has been automated by making the block into a roller. As the roller turns, the fabric moves continuously under it. A different roller is needed for each colour. The design is built up by a series of print rollers arranged around a drum. When the fabric is fed between the rollers and the drum the areas of colour meet to produce the complete design. This is called **roller printing** and is a relatively cheap method. However, the detail produced is sometimes not as fine as some specifications require and another method has to be used.

Screen printing is another method of printing fabric. It works rather like **stencilling**. An **image**

■ Screen printing – how a design can be built up

(the design) is cut out of a thin sheet of film. A screen is made by covering a frame with a fine fabric, such as silk or nylon. The film is placed on top of the screen, with the design facing downward. The fabric is put under the screen and dye is pushed through the open parts of the screen. The design is printed on the fabric underneath.

Transfer printing

In this method, the dye is changed from a liquid to a gas or vapour. The dye then penetrates (soaks into) the fibre more easily and quickly. The design is printed onto paper using disperse dyes. The paper is laid on top of the fabric and heat is applied. The heat causes the dye to change from its solid state on the paper to a vapour, and then back to a solid state on the fabric. This is called **sublimation** and it works because:

➤ the dye in vapour form is not attracted to the paper, but it is strongly attracted to the fabric (particularly one made from polyester fibres), so it moves onto the fabric and is absorbed
➤ the colour is set into the fabric which transfers the print to the fabric.

The advantages of this method are:
➤ it is relatively cheap
➤ it produces a colourfast result without the need for another process
➤ water is not required, therefore there is no risk of pollution from the disposal of liquid waste.

Designing and colour

The photos show how printed fabrics are used in different situations. All the fabrics used are printed, they will all have been designed by someone originally. How might this have been done? Each individual designer has their own way

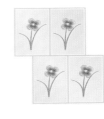

■ How printed fabrics are used in different situations

Planning Decisions are made about how to use the material collected, how to set out the design, the number of colours to use and the technical possibilities of reproducing the design. An example of a decision which has to be made for some fabrics, particularly those to be used for interior design and soft furnishing, is the size and repeat of a particular motif or pattern. This is because the design must fit into the width of the cloth. The diagrams show examples of design repeats.

Full drop repeat   Half drop repeat   Brick repeat

■ Design repeats

The effects created by the pattern or design repeats in the diagrams are a vertical stripe for the half-drop and a horizontal stripe in the case of the brick. The repeats are very important because the fabric may be spoilt if lines are formed which were not part of the original design. A designer will choose the type of repeat which looks best for a particular design and will show this by including one complete repeat and parts of the design around it when submitting ideas to the manufacturer.

of working but they all share common starting points if they are putting together proposals for fabric manufacturers. Many designers are artists who produce designs for a variety of products, e.g. wallpapers, household linens, fabrics for clothing.

Gathering ideas and information about the brief are essential first steps in making sure that what is produced is appropriate. Knowledge of the style favoured by the fabric producer, the image they wish to portray and the fashion emphasis of the time are all important pieces of information. Designing can then start, using that information as the 'needs' of the situation.

Starting points

Inspiration Photographs or illustrations can be used to find shapes and structures which could form the basis of a design. The designers featured in the case studies in Section 5 describe different sources of inspiration and how they use them.

— *Task*

Produce a design to submit to a manufacturer who wishes to launch a range of bed linen using the theme 'The Millennium – the year 2000'.
a Show the source(s) of your inspiration and explain why they are appropriate.
b Sketch your ideas and include design details such as colours, outlines, repeats etc.
c Communicate your ideas using a mood board (samples which illustrate the image or mood your suggestions will create) and any other suitable medium, as though you were submitting a proposal to a particular manufacturer.

3.11 Textiles and environmental issues

*T*here is increasing interest worldwide in how best to use land and resources in order to preserve them for future generations. The production of most fibres, whether natural or manufactured, involves land, or **finite** resources from the land, in one way or another. Finite resources are limited, for example, when coal or oil runs out there is no more. Throughout your study of textile product development you will be learning about decisions that other people have made about the use of textiles, and also making decisions yourself.

The information given in Section 2 about the production and performance characteristics (qualities) of various fibres will help you make decisions about the best textile to use to meet specific requirements. It also will help you to judge the appropriateness of other people's choices.

The following information illustrates some other factors which can be considered when looking at the use of textiles generally.

Land required

Diagram 1 shows a comparison between the amount of acrylic fibre produced in the UK in 1985 and the area of pasture that would be needed by the sheep that would provide that amount of wool.

Diagram 2 shows a comparison between the 8000 hectares (20,000 acres) used to produce wood-pulp from which viscose fibre is produced and the amount of arable land needed to produce an equivalent amount of cotton.

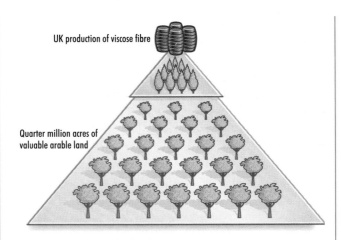

■ Diagram 2 Viscose fibre and cotton production

These two diagrams highlight the environmental benefit claims made for the use of manufactured fibres.

Other information supplied about fibres includes reference to the effect bad weather conditions have on crops used to produce some natural fibres, and the fact that manufactured fibres can be **engineered** to meet specific criteria e.g. performance and aesthetic characteristics such as softness, warmth, absorbency, colour etc.

— *Task*

Use the information about performance and aesthetic characteristics of fibres and fabrics given in Section 2 to present a balanced approach to choosing and using textiles. Include sketches and/or diagrams to illustrate the points you make.

Recyling textiles

Provided the subject is approached in a professional way recycling can be a very interesting theme for a design-and-make task which would be suitable to submit for assessment.

What is meant by 'professional'?

Lyn Luxton of Huso Huso can illustrate this. Huso Huso is based in Exeter and is a successful business which makes products using recycled textiles. Lyn Luxton says:

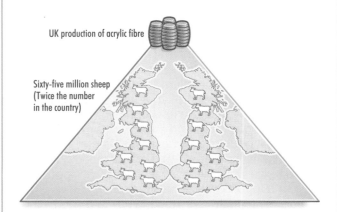

■ Diagram 1 Acrylic fibre and wool production

'The main things which contribute to that success are making sure that the products are capable of competing in the general market place – not one solely concerned with recycled products – and the understanding that marketing in textile products is very tough. The products have to meet a need in order to identify an opportunity to produce a saleable item. In addition the products must meet the quality standard expected by the consumer in the general market place.

'Consumers will not buy products which are of inferior quality simply because they make use of recycled textiles, although to some customers the "green image" is an added benefit. However, the products must stand on their own in the same way as the products with which they are competing.'

What other information is available?

Case study: Waste Watch

Waste Watch is a national agency for the promotion and development of action on waste reduction and recycling. It is part funded by the Department of the Environment. Waste Watch provides information about textile reclamation and recycling; the address is Waste Watch, Hobart House, Grosvenor Place, London SW1X 7AE.

The energy efficiency Best Practice programme

The Best Practice programme is part of the Government's commitment to improving energy efficiency in the national economy. In the Department of Environment this is case study number 181. It illustrates a Best Practice programme in the textile industry. Information about the case study is given below.

The company featured in case study 181 is called Evergreen. On the right, John Parkinson, a partner in Evergreen, summarizes the operation.

Comments from Evergreen

We started Evergreen in 1990 after many months of planning. Evergreen aims to produce attractive yarns, fabrics and garments with a reduced environmental impact by using a high proportion of recycled fibre. We avoid environmentally harmful processes whenever we can, and ensure that the chemicals used in the unavoidable treatments are the mildest possible. Attention to energy efficiency is an important part of our green philosophy.

This case study has quantified the savings we are making and confirmed the energy and environmental benefits of recycling textiles. Consumers are becoming more and more aware of the high energy inputs into textiles, and other environmental drawbacks, and I would advise other textiles manufacturers to consider such factors. An additional benefit is that the recycled fibre usually has a lower cost than new fibre, and expensive processes like dyeing are unnecessary. Consequently our finished products are competitively priced.

Research and development into other areas of environmentally responsible textile processing continues at Evergreen. Since the data were gathered for this study we have introduced ranges of recycled synthetics and cotton in addition to wool.

Evergreen

Evergreen is a small privately owned company which has developed a range of yarns, fabrics and finished products using a high proportion of recycled wool fibre. Traditionally the recycled fibre sector of the woollen industry has been regarded as the bottom end of the trade. Evergreen is attempting to reverse this attitude by manufacturing high quality, fashionable garments which do not only require much less energy than their new wool equivalents, but cause less pollution and make use of a waste product which might otherwise go to landfill sites.

Case Study Objectives

To quantify the energy and other savings arising from the use of recycled fibre in manufacturing knitting yarns, fabric and/or garments.

Case Study Summary

ENERGY EFFICIENCY
DEPARTMENT OF THE ENVIRONMENT

Many of the processes involved in the production of woollen material from virgin fibre use large amounts of energy. However, when recycled fibre is used many of the more energy intensive processes are not needed and significant energy savings can be achieved.

Significant environmental benefits can be achieved because many of the processes are not repeated. This means less effluent is produced, less fresh water is used and use is made of old garments which would have otherwise gone to landfill sites.

Why is this a Best Practice programme?

The outline and the benefits of this particular process are shown below.

Background

Although natural textile fibres such as wool are considered more environmentally friendly than their synthetic counterparts, the production, transportation and processing of wool into a finished garment consume relatively large amounts of energy. However, by using recycled fibre rather than new wool, a large proportion of this energy can be saved because the recycled waste has already undergone several of the most energy-intensive processes and these do not need to be repeated.

The manufacturing process

Evergreen operates a system whereby it retains ownership of the product through the complete manufacturing process, although some of the manufacturing steps may be sub-contracted. This means that the company can keep control of quality and cost.

Generally, the manufacturing process, from reclaimed fibre to finished garment, consists of the following steps, not all of which are carried out by Evergreen:

Raw materials

Textile mills such as Evergreen buy their raw material directly from charity outlets (post consumer waste), from knitting factories (post industrial waste) or from rag merchants. The single-colour material in this waste is then sorted into 40 standard shades.

Rag pulling

Rags are put through a machine which has counter-rotating rollers covered in spikes which tear the rags into their constituent fibre, known as shoddy. These machines are capable of processing 80 kg of rags per hour.

Blending

Blending, a fibre mixing process, is mostly done by hand at Evergreen.

Carding

Carding disentangles, cleans and intermixes the fibres to make a continuous web of approximately parallel fibres. A condenser on the end of the card produces discrete ropes of parallel fibre without twist (slubbings).

Spinning

The spinning process involves drawing out the fibres and then inserting a twist to produce a yarn. To produce a stronger yarn, two ends of yarn are folded and then twisted together.

Post consumer waste prior to sorting

Rag pulling machine

Spinning frame

Waste is sorted into 40 standard shades

Slubbings being wound onto bobbins

Weaving or knitting

These processes produce fabric or knitted garment pieces.

Fabric finishing

The finished processes involve setting woven fabric to width, applying a colour and improving its handle and other properties.

Making up garments

This is the final part of the manufacturing process and produces the finished garments.

Energy and cost savings

The use of recycled fibre eliminates the need for:

- transportation of apparel wool from overseas, usually Australasia;
- raw wool scouring – a washing process to remove dirt and animal secretions etc;
- carbonizing – a process to remove contaminants from wool;
- dyeing.

The finished product

Garment quality

Extensive laboratory testing was carried out on samples from the Evergreen range, which proved that the quality of these items is not significantly below major national and international standards. Nevertheless, in certain respects the wear performance of several of the fabrics was below that which would normally be considered acceptable. However, consumers who choose garments made from recycled material may be prepared to accept a reduced garment life, or less than perfect appearance, in return for the environmental benefits.

Before you start a task involving recycling, read the following to make sure that this is something in which you are sufficiently interested to carry out the research, to source and prepare the raw materials and to design and make products which will have a market.

The benefits of textile recycling (sometimes called **textile recovery**) are that it:

➤ can reduce the amount of landfill space used (Textiles create particular problems in landfill sites because some textiles, particularly some synthetic fibres, will not decompose and woollen garments produce methane gas which contributes to the global warming, although wool will decompose.)

➤ reduces the demand for **virgin** (new, unused) resources

➤ helps the nation's balance of payments because of the need to import less

➤ reduces pollution and saves energy because fibres do not have to be imported from abroad in such large quantities

➤ provides energy savings in processing, for example dyeing and other processes involved in producing new fabrics do not have to be carried out

➤ produces less **effluent** (liquid waste from manufacturing processes) e.g. raw wool has to be washed thoroughly using large volumes of water

➤ brings about a reduction in use of dyes and agents used to fix colour, some of which may be a risk to the environment.

If you decide to go ahead with a task in this area you will need to put together a brief which describes:

➤ what you are going to do, and why

➤ the product(s) that you have in mind, their purpose

➤ who will use/buy it

➤ the market opportunities.

Be realistic about what can be achieved in school. For example, it is obvious that the machinery used to reclaim fibres is not available. However, careful selection, cleaning and taking apart of used textile products can provide inspiration for a range of 'new' items such as hats, bags and many other saleable ideas.

The sequence of the stages involved in the manufacture of textiles and textile products are shown in this flow diagram.

- Fibre production
- Yarn production
- Fabric production (weaving/knitting)
- Finishing (applying colour)
- Manufacture of textile products
- Retailing
- Purchasing and use

Commercial production

The commercial production of textiles and textile products involves many types of companies, different product types and volumes of production and a number of different manufacturing environments. In the production of fibres, yarns and fabrics some highly **automated** methods of production are used but in some other areas of production it is a different story.

For example, the introduction of automated methods is more gradual in making textile products than in some other areas of manufacturing. Many systems of production are still highly labour-intensive (people do the work). An important reason for this is that whatever product is being made from textiles, sewing and other joining methods form an essential part of their construction. These methods are, generally, still best done **manually** (by hand, using human labour). Research in automation is being carried out to discover if and how motor-driven devices can replace manual operators.

■ An automatic belt-loop attaching machine

Research into automation

The aim of research in this field is to find a mechanical handling system where the movements of the robots can be reprogrammed as and when necessary. There any many difficulties to overcome. One of these is the need to change top and bottom threads on machines. At the moment this can only be done manually. Other aspects which slow down the move towards automation include:

> **the properties of the raw materials** Fabrics are limp, they are flexible and bend in all directions. This makes it very difficult to invent automated equipment (such as jigs etc.) which can produce effective and high-quality results.
> **fabric thickness** Within one product there may be a number of different thicknesses to be sewn.
> **extensibility (ability to stretch) of individual fabrics** This depends not only on the property of particular fibres but also the way the fabric is cut. For example, where the fabric must be capable of forming a curve, as in an armhole, the fabric is cut on the **bias** for maximum stretch.

These are the main reasons why sewing remains the best way of joining fabric together. In technological terms, a stitch is a **flexible joint**.

— Task —

a Look at a variety of textile products. Choose *two* different ones from the following list: bags, scarves, garments of different types, flags, tents, wall-hangings, containers/carriers, hats etc.
b Examine each one to find out:
  > how it is joined together
  > why the method(s) used were chosen
  > whether the methods do the job well, i.e. perform the function required satisfactorily.

This is the simple way of discovering how well a product fulfils its purpose. This is sometimes called attribute analysis. In this case you are finding out whether the methods of joining used are appropriate for the fabric used for the products you have chosen and the use for which the products are intended (this will involve thinking about the use of the product, its performance requirements, the market (i.e. the consumer) it appeals to and so on.

*F*ashion design and product development must work together to produce the variety and quality of garments demanded by consumers, when they are required and at a price which consumers are willing to pay. This co-operation is the basis of clothing technology and the successful marketing of garments.

There are three main factors which designers and clothing manufacturers must have in mind when producing garments.
➤ The aesthetic, functional and commercial (i.e. the financial return required) qualities required of the materials used in production.
➤ The functional, social, cultural and psychological characteristics which consumers expect from garments.
➤ How designing and production processes of cutting, sewing, joining and pressing can fulfil each of the requirements detailed above in the time available.

In your textiles technology work in school you also need to apply an understanding of these. They could be in the form of a checklist using the headings 'aesthetics', 'performance' and 'price' as the aspects which should be checked to make sure that ideas are possible, achievable and likely to be successful. The importance of each will vary according to the product being developed and made. For example, for a wall-hanging, aesthetics will be the most important aspect, followed by the other two, whereas for a pair of school trousers, performance will be most important.

Categories of clothing

Fashionable items

What is fashion? Generally it is something which is popular at a particular time. Fashion designers have to be able to **predict** (tell in advance) what will be popular at a later stage in time, which means that they have to work ahead of the market. Clothing and clothing-related products shown in a particular season, for example a winter season, have to be designed during or just after the previous winter season.

Categories of fashion include:
➤ **couture**, which is a very exclusive, highly individual example of fashion. The garments set the trend for a season.
➤ **bespoke production**, where garments are made for individual clients according to size and requirements.
➤ **street fashion**, where the clothing chosen and worn by individuals and groups says something about their interests, tastes, and attitudes. Street fashion tends to have a short life, which means that the sectors of the clothing industry that supply this market must be capable of changing quickly.
➤ **staple garments**, such as shirts, underwear, leisure and sports garments, uniforms and workwear; although these are not subject to rapid changes consumers expect a degree of fashion in all garments now.

— *Task*

Look at these photos of garments.
Which category of fashion does each belong to?

*T*he information below describes a typical system used commercially in textile product development. The stages involved in the system are illustrated in the flow diagram. The information gathered at each stage of the process is used to adapt and perfect other stages. This helps to make sure that high-quality products are made and are available at the time and in the amounts that the client or consumer wants them. This is called feedback information. The arrows on the right-hand side of the diagram show when feedback happens and the direction in which the information is going.

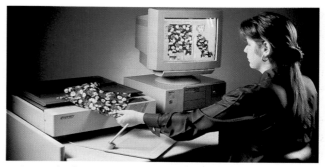

■ Concept development using a computer

What happens at each stage?

1 Research

Ideas for designs come from a variety of sources, including:

➤ fairs and shows which are held in various cities during the year, e.g. the *Premiere Vision* Show of fabrics held in Paris; Interstoff, a fabric fair held in Düsseldorf

➤ other people's ideas e.g. looking at the shapes and styles of garments which sell in cities known for their fashion images such as Florence, Italy; Paris, France; New York, Los Angeles, USA
➤ inspiration such as the shapes and textures found on buildings in nature, on the streets etc.
➤ services which supply forecasts of the colours and shapes that are going to be popular.

2 Design concept (idea(s))

The concept is developed by sketching and modelling (with computer/card/colour combinations etc.). Sometimes a garment made from calico or muslin is modelled. This is called a **toile**.

   Careful checking takes place at this stage to improve and adapt the concept. Trials and tests are carried out to check the best colours, shapes, types of fabric, surface decoration etc. The feedback information from these trials and tests is used to improve the concept.

3 Market screening

Checks are carried out to make sure there is a market for the concept. They also identify the type of person who will buy it – this is the **market segment** the concept is aimed at.

4 Prototype of trial pattern

Knowledge of types of body shapes in the identified segment of the market, raw materials and equipment and anthropometrics (measurement of the human body) is needed and applied here.

5 Sample

The sample is made up by a skilled machinist using the **prototype** pattern. The machinist finds out how the garment can be constructed most economically to give the best result and a good fit.

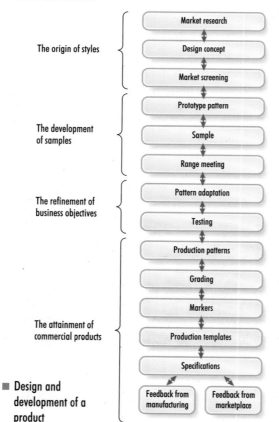

The origin of styles
- Market research
- Design concept
- Market screening

The development of samples
- Prototype pattern
- Sample
- Range meeting

The refinement of business objectives
- Pattern adaptation
- Testing

The attainment of commercial products
- Production patterns
- Grading
- Markers
- Production templates
- Specifications

Feedback from manufacturing   Feedback from marketplace

■ Design and development of a product

6 Range meeting

At this meeting, decisions are made based on the sample garments. Members of the design, production and marketing teams take part. The garment(s) are critically examined to see whether they can be produced for the costs forecast, i.e. the estimates of labour costs and raw materials and the contribution to overheads and profit which could be made by sales. It is at this stage that decisions are made about which garments are to be developed.

7 Pattern adaptation

Alterations are made as a result of the range meeting. These can be concerned with ways of reducing costs, examining alternative fabrics or correcting fitting problems. Further discussion between members of the range meeting may take place to plan the sequence of construction for bulk production, to consider further investment (e.g. any new equipment or training which may be required and whether it can be afforded).

The plans for production must include details of:
> **input** (raw materials, equipment, personnel etc.)
> **process** (manufacturing stages, control of them in order to achieve success)
> **output** (amounts produced, delivery requirements and dates).

8 Testing

The performance characteristics and quality must be checked to make sure the garment fits its purpose. This includes testing durability, care details, aspects of comfort, resistance to wear, fluids, sunlight and whatever else is appropriate.

9 Production patterns

These show seams, grain lines and other relevant pattern symbols.

10 Grading

This is carried out using information gathered about the sizes and body shapes of the target market. The pattern sizes are increased and decreased to provide a range of sizes to suit the market.

11 Marker planning

This is a bit like fitting the pieces of a jigsaw puzzle together. The pattern pieces are irregular, which means that the marker must discover which pieces

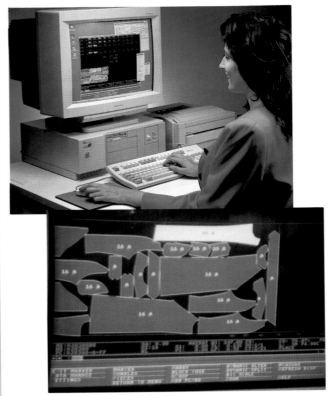

■ Computer-aided marker planning

fit together, making sure wastage of fabric is kept to a minimum. When this is achieved, it is called a **lay**. In addition, the plan must make sure the surface pile of fabrics and those with surface decoration such as stripes and checks lay the correct way.

Templates for such things as button-hole markings may also be produced at this stage, to save time and labour costs during construction. When the plan has been worked out a cutting marker is made. This marker is spread on the top layer of the fabric. This is sometimes referred to as **spreading**.

12 Specifications

The requirements of the design first identified by the designer are finalized at this stage. The details are very precise, so that what has been designed will be produced.

13 Feedback

This may come from the manufacturing process. It may also come from sales figures and knowledge of consumer reaction.

Cutting

The garment pieces are cut from the fabric, using the cutting marker as the outline. Sometimes this is in two stages, firstly rough cutting which separates the pieces and secondly accurate cutting of individual shapes. To ensure that garments fit properly and can be made up satisfactorily, the pieces must be cut accurately to the shapes of the pattern.

Different types of cutting tools are used according to the number of layers of fabric in the lay and the bulk of garments to be cut. Each layer of fabric is called a ply. Hand shears are normally used for one or two layers of fabric, i.e. single ply or double plies. When there are more plies cutting is more likely to be done with a straight knife, a round knife or a band knife. Automated machines such as a die cutting machine are sometimes used. This machine has cutting tools (the die) which are the exact shape of the garment pieces; the pieces are stamped out on a base plate. These machines are expensive and are therefore used only for garments

which remain the same for a long period of time, such as work clothes and overalls, etc. There are also computer-controlled fully automatic cutting machines such as the one shown in the photo.

Laser cutters are not usually used in the clothing industry, although they are beginning to be used for cutting sails which are nearly always cut in single ply.

Notches or position marks have to be made on the garment pieces to provide guidelines for accurate sewing. The marks must not be visible on the finished garment. **Hot notchers** contain a heating element which scorches fibres slightly, to prevent the mark disappearing or fraying.

Construction

The next step in production is construction, which means putting the garment together. There are several different systems used.

1 Make-through

Skilled machinists carry out the main construction of the garment and other machinists do the overlocking of seams, button-holes and pressing.

2 The progressive bundle system

The garment pieces are tied in bundles for each operation and taken to the machinist who is going to carry out that operation. The sewing room is arranged in sections according to the operations. These include the production of sub-components,

■ A skilled cutter cutting a stack of sleeves

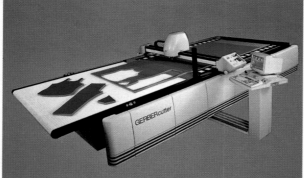

■ A computer-controlled cutting machine

■ The progressive bundle system in action

such as pockets, sleeves etc. There is space around each section to store bundles which are waiting to be dealt with so that time is not wasted. These spaces are sometimes referred to as **buffer zones**.

3 The unit production system (UPS)

This system consists of a power-driven loop with work-places spaced at regular intervals around the outside. Cut work is fed onto the line, with garments on hangers and smaller pieces in baskets. Each work-station has an operator who completes a particular part of the construction. The garments are transferred on hangers around the system until construction is complete. Each operator carries out the same operation over and over again.

4 The Toyota sewing system

This is similar to the UPS, except that in this case the operators stand up to work. The machines are raised on pedestals and laid out in a U-shape. In each U a team of about ten skilled operators work together on one bundle at a time. A **production manager** provides continuous feedback to the team, showing **target output** throughout the day. The U-shape of the work station and the close relationships which develop within the team make this a successful system in that motivation of the team is strong and absenteeism is low. The cost involved in setting up is less than for UPS but the output tends to be lower.

■ The Toyota sewing system

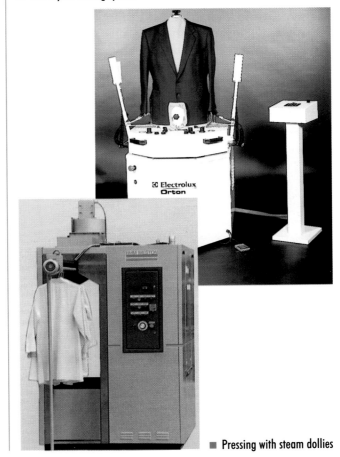
■ Pressing with steam dollies

Pressing

After completion, finished garments are pressed, ready for sale. The two methods used are dry pressing and steam pressing. Various equipment is used, chosen according to the finish required and the shape to be pressed. The two photos show steam dollies which are used to press whole garments.

— *Task*

Imagine you are part of a team of workers making up a simple shirt.

a Work in a group of six people (you and five others).

b Plan a unit production system (UPS) for making up the shirt. Identify the operation each worker must carry out. Estimate the time each operation should take in order that a good-quality 'job' is done but no time is wasted.

*I*t would not be possible to get in and out of garments without fastenings. Sometimes the fastenings are special design features, built in by the designer. Fastenings are chosen primarily on the basis of their functions and the performance requirements of a particular garment.

Types of fastenings

Buttons and button-holes

These can be almost any shape and colour. They are made from a variety of materials such as nylon, polyester, wood, metal, leather or mother of pearl. For successful fastening the hole must be big enough to take the button. The material used must be resistant to heat, washing and dry cleaning.

Hooks and eyes, hooks and bars

These are used mainly at the top of zips. They reduce the strain and pressure on the top of a zip.

Press studs

These are used a great deal in baby clothes and denim jeans. The two parts of each stud must be positioned to match up exactly, otherwise the stud will not perform as it is intended to do.

Hook and loop, for example Velcro

This is made from two woven polyamide tapes. One is covered with very fine hooks and the other with very fine loops. These interlock when the strips are pressed together and a firm fastening is made.

There is a story about how Velcro was invented which may or may not be true. The scientist who invented this fastening noticed that when his dog brushed against thistle-type plants the burrs from the plants stuck to the dog's hair and were very difficult to remove. This is said to have inspired the invention of Velcro.

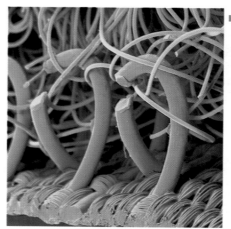

■ A coloured scanning electron micrograph picture of the nylon hooks and loops used in Velcro

■ Velcro used as a fastening for a pair of gloves

■ A toggle fastening

■ 'Velcro' in nature

Tack buttons, snap fasteners and rivets

Some garments, such as jeans, require extra strong fastenings. Tack buttons and snap fasteners made of metal can match the durability and strength of the denim from which jeans are made. Rivets reinforce (strengthen further) the buttons and snaps and also look decorative. Rivets are characteristic features of jeans.

■ Rivets are used to strengthen jeans

Zip fasteners

Zips are used on a number of garments to close openings. Each zip has two edges which mesh together and cannot be pulled apart. Each edge is attached to tape which is sewn to the garment. There are two types of zip, the *invisible* zip and the *continuous* type. Invisible zips have the teeth turned onto the inside of the garment; when this type of zip is attached to the garment the stitching is not visible. Continuous zips can be applied as two separate pieces, as in men's trousers. This means making up is easier because, generally, each leg of a pair of trousers is assembled separately and then the crutch seam is joined and the zip is attached.

— *Task* —

Investigate the variety of fastenings used in textile products. Notice how they are used and whether their use is effective in each case. Record your findings in your notebook.

4.6 Surface decoration

*T*he two main methods of surface decoration used in textile manufacturing are sewn decorations and pressed decorations.

Sewn decorations

The simplest of decorations is made with one or two lines of **two-thread lock-stitch**. Saddle stitching can be used to produce an appearance of hand-stitching on jacket edges.

Gathering is used to dispose of fullness and make frills. Sewing **tucks** into fabric also reduces fullness and can be used to produce particular features in the shaping of a garment.

Piping is another surface decoration used in sewing. A strip of fabric is cut on the bias to give maximum stretch. Then a piece of cord is covered with the fabric and attached to the main fabric item to produce a firm seam or edge. **Smocking**, **shirring** and **quilting** can also be used to decorate large areas of fabric or a garment.

Smocking is a method of disposing of fullness whilst shirring uses elastic thread to take up fullness in waists, cuffs etc. The night-dress in the photo shows an example of smocking.

Quilting involves using two-thread lock-stitch to sew two plies of fabric together with **wadding** in between them. A designer who chooses to quilt the surface of a fabric will choose wadding which meets the needs of the situation. There are many different weights and thicknesses of wadding, which is sometimes called **batting**. The designer will consider the degree of insulation required, the cost, the bulk supplied by the wadding, the shape and dimensions of the quilting design and then choose

■ Quilted textiles

the wadding which best meets the aesthetic and performance requirements of the product. The photos show different uses of quilted fabrics.

Pressed decorations

Pleats are the best example of pressed decorations. These are set into the fabric, in the desired shape and form, and pressed into place. They also dispose of fullness and can be sewn into place after pressing. The simplest pleat is the crease put into trouser legs.

Joining

Another important decision the designer must make is how to join or decorate the component parts of any textile item. The decision must be based on the performance requirements of the item and the functional properties of the materials from which it is made. The choice of stitch for a particular purpose must be appropriate so that a high-quality product is made. Classification and terminology of stitch types are covered in the reference: British Standard 3870: Part 1 1982.

— Task

Look in clothing outlets of different types e.g. high street chain stores, market stalls, smaller individual stores, to find as many different examples as possible of the disposal of fullness in garments. Record your findings in your notebook. Use your findings to help you to decide whether the method of disposing of fullness affects the selling price of a garment.

■ Smocking on a party dress

4.7 Working efficiently

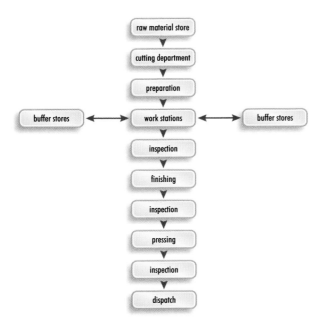

■ A material flow pattern in a factory

Material flow

The sequence and rate at which raw materials are processed into final products ready for distribution must be planned very carefully, to make sure that the most efficient system is adopted on the factory floor. The diagram shows a typical flow pattern.

Method study

Investigations are made into particular operations to find the best and most economical method for carrying them out. The objectives of method study are to improve and develop working methods, equipment, products and working environments. During the investigations the comfort of the operator is considered, as well as the working environment, the working methods and equipment used. The example shows five stages in a sewing operation which could form the basis of a study.

Ergonomics

Ergonomics is the study of the efficiency of the people in the work-place. The objective is to discover the situations which produce the best quality work, most economically, with the minimum of stress being placed on the worker. Ergonomically-designed work-places reduce stress and tiredness and increase concentration and efficiency. The factors which contribute to ergonomically-designed work-places include:

➤ **anthropometric design** Equipment and work spaces are designed to fit the dimensions and movements of the human body. This covers such things as the height of working tables, chairs which support the spine, and the layout of working areas. The space required to ensure comfortable working conditions depends on the equipment required and the operation being carried out. A good example is the guideline that a seated person carrying out a sewing operation should not be more than 20 cm away from the equipment and their eyes should be about 40 cm from the point of the needle.

➤ **control of the environment** This involves controlling the degree to which the work is tiring, boring, dull and tedious and the length of the time between breaks. Lighting, air conditioning, noise and pollution control are also considered. The aim is to provide restful, attractive and comfortable working spaces.

Task

Investigate the heights of the tables and support given by the chairs you use when sewing. How well do they suit your requirements? Carry out tests to find out. Record your opinions and conclusions in your notebook.

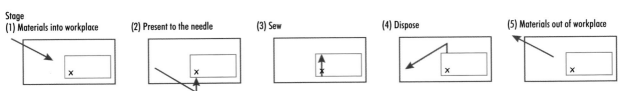

■ Five stages in a sewing operation

4.8 Quality assurance and quality control

What is the difference?

It is helpful first to define quality and what it means to the people involved in the chain of development of a product, from the concept stage right through to buying. Expectations relating to quality vary according to the part of the development a person is involved in. The consumer, for example, expects a product to be fit for the purpose for which it is intended, and considers its performance, price and aesthetic qualities in order to assess its quality.

The designer and manufacturer assess quality by how well the product meets the specification. This is referred to as **conformance** to the specification. When a product does not conform to the specifications at any stage this is **non-conformance**. Non-conformance of any kind is expensive for the producer because extra steps have to be taken to put the product right.

Quality assurance

Quality assurance is achieved by using a system for checking conformance at every stage of the production, manufacture and retailing of a product. There are specific criteria to be followed at every stage from product design, raw materials, production processes and packaging, through to customer service to make sure a product conforms to the specification.

Quality control

Quality control involves the use of checking procedures at every stage of development to make sure the product will meet the specification. Checking for quality involves the production and use of clear instructions and criteria for every stage, and testing and inspecting to make sure the required standards of quality are being met.

Quality control operates in each of the following stages:

> **market research** studying consumer requirements
> **design**
> **fabric specification** including details of the total length and number of pieces, width and weight of fabric, weave structure, fibre composition, shade and surface decoration (with a sample to show the exact requirements)
> **specification for garment or item** including details of style features (with an illustration), the fabrics which may be used, trims required, size scale, stitch and seam specifications, relevant details of the manufacturing process
> **manufacturing specification** containing details of each process and operation, the method to use and keypoints relating to quality
> **management of production** involving making sure that the materials and manufacturing processes are capable of meeting the design requirements; it is particularly important to check that quality products can be manufactured when the scale of production is changed e.g. when bulk or mass production is planned
> **meeting standards** understanding and accepting that everyone involved must carry responsibility for meeting the standards of quality required in their operation; for example an operator has responsibilities to reject imperfect work when it is presented, to carry out the work by the specified method, to make sure items are completed to the required standard, to re-do faulty items which are returned
> **inspection and checks** consisting of three main aims at this stage: to make sure the consumer gets perfect items, to safeguard the company's reputation and to provide feedback information about failure to meet the specification.

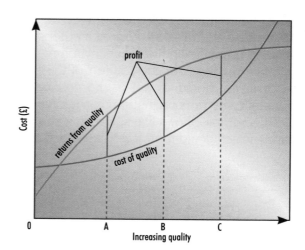

■ The relationship between quality and profit

86

Quality is an essential part of successful marketing. The diagram at the bottom of page 86 shows how this works.

Lower profit results when sales are low or the costs of production are too high. This shows that, although it is important to produce high-quality goods, a great deal of analysis and planning must form part of the design and production of a product to make sure adequate profit is made from its sale.

The photo shows a man's coat which has been taken apart. Remember this is sometimes called disassembly (or de-construction) or attribute analysis. Manufacturers sometimes carry this out on an item when there have been lots of complaints about it not meeting the level of performance expected of it or when they wish to compare it with a similar product made by a competitor.

Jacket pieces
A Back (left)
B Back (right)
C Side panel (left)
D Front left
E Front right
F Front facing left

G Front facing right
H Left top sleeve
I Left under sleeve
J Pocket (× 2)
K Breast pocket
L Top collar
M Stand

O Under collar
Linings
1 Back (right)
2 Side panel (right)
3 Front right
4 Right under sleeve
5 Right top sleeve

6 Pocket (× 2)
7 Breast pocket
8 Shoulder pads (× 2)
9 Top sleeve pads (× 2)
10 canvas interlining

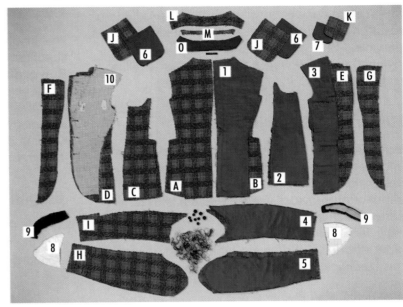

■ A man's jacket disassembled

Tasks

1 Work in a group of four. Choose a textile product which you can disassemble (take apart).
Old textile products for this task can be bought for very little at jumble sales, but for health reasons they should be washed or cleaned before you start your task. An alternative is to use items which you no longer need or like.

Blouses, shirts and jeans are all suitable garments to choose. Knitted items are less suitable because they are more difficult to dissect. If threads break it is acceptable to estimate their length. Fusible interlining usually peels off very easily and can be examined, but any foam-backed fabric should be left as it is and the property it gives to the item should be described.

2 Decide on roles, e.g. one person can be in charge of recording the evidence collected, one person can count and remove trimmings etc., one person can unpick seams, and one person can measure pieces of the product, the threads etc. used.

3 Describe the product and its function. What was the target market? What do you think the specification for its development was?

4 Discuss the extent to which it meets 'fitness for purpose'.

5 Take the product apart. Be very organized in your approach. *At each stage* discuss and record what you find. Areas of discussion should include why particular fabrics, trimmings etc. were used and what function they fulfil.

6 Tease some of the fibres out. Examine them under a microscope to see if you can identify them.

7 Use the information about quality control and quality assurance to help you suggest how quality was built into the item. Were the quality control and quality assurance procedures effective? Do you think the item meets the specification set for it?

Rapid (or quick) response

What does 'rapid response' mean and what does it have to do with textile products? The modern consumer wants textiles items to be available at the time and in the quantities required. In short, the modern consumer will not wait for production to catch up with demand. Rapid or quick response provides the items when and where they are required at a price which the consumer is willing to pay.

How does this work?

Success depends on the ability to transfer information rapidly throughout the chain of design, production, distribution and retailing. The information provides evidence which is used to perfect each stage in the whole operation. It is especially important that information from the point of sale should be available quickly, because this feedback ensures that the items needed are produced.

Computerized systems are generally used to transfer the information, whether it is from the point of sale or from part of the production system, such as the sewing room.

Electronic data interchange (EDI)

This involves agreements between retailers and suppliers about standardized computer activities. **Bar-coding** is one example. The USA is ahead in this type of development at the moment. The advantages include the ability to capture precise information on consumer purchasing at a Stock Keeping Unit (SKU) and use this information to make reordering quicker, easier and more efficient.

Just-in-time and Just-in-case

These are names given to systems for storing and sourcing raw materials and other things needed for production.

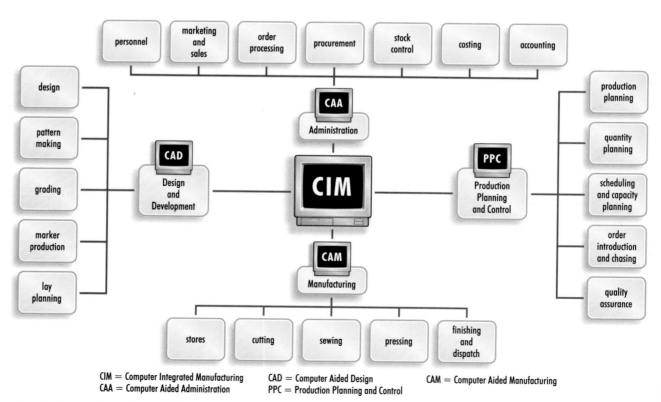

CIM = Computer Integrated Manufacturing   CAD = Computer Aided Design   CAM = Computer Aided Manufacturing
CAA = Computer Aided Administration   PPC = Production Planning and Control

Just-in-time means that whatever stock is needed is available just at the time it is needed. Stock is not kept on shelves where it is not making money. The reference earlier in this book to dyers dying cloth only when particular colours are ordered is one example. The system must be very carefully organized because if materials are not available when they are needed production is held up and more money is lost.

Just-in-case means items are kept in stock in case they are needed. Manufacturers tend not to use this system unless they are sure the items will be used fairly quickly. Items in stock for any length of time reduce financial returns and can cause financial difficulties.

Use of computers

The processing of data by computer can be very fast and efficient. In theory it should be possible to link all the different processes involved in production together in one system, under the control of one computer. However, this kind of **integration**, where information from every department is received in the same network, is an expensive investment. An information system of this kind is shown in the diagram on page 88.

The information systems which could be involved are:
- **computer integrated manufacture** (CIM)
- **computer-aided administration** (CAA)
- **computer-aided design** (CAD)
- **production, planning and control** (PPC)
- **computer-aided manufacture** (CAM).

Examples of what happens now

CAD

Computer programs are used in design and pattern development in many parts of the textile industry. The photos show some examples.

CAM

The photos below show one example of computer-aided manufacture.

■ Computer-aided manufacture (CAM) being used for lay planning

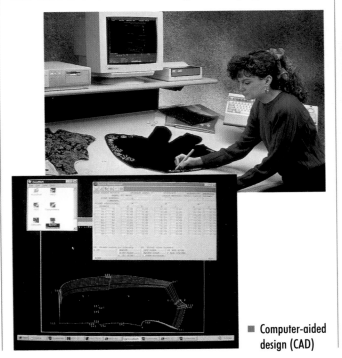

■ Computer-aided design (CAD)

— Task

Draw a design for a sample product such as a purse. Include the dimensions of the product. Reproduce this design using a computer. Ask a graphics expert to help you if you do not know how to do it.

*C*lothing is a basic need for all humans. It should fulfil each of the following functions in relation to the specific requirements of a particular person.

Identification

The clothing a person wears can indicate the particular group to which that person belongs within society or a part of the world. Examples of such clothing include traditional costumes and uniforms. Street fashion and punk style identify less distinct groups, as do the team scarves and hats worn by football fans. Some clothing is associated with a particular period in time, such as Victorian, Edwardian, 1960s, 1980s etc. Costume designers for the theatre must be able to understand the nature of each character for whom a costume is to be designed. The costume must communicate additional information about the character to the audience.

Decoration

The clothing a person wears gives some indication of their personality and individuality. The type of decoration and the image portrayed can vary according to the popular fashion of the day and the culture.

Protection

Clothing is needed for protection against the elements such as sun, heat, wind, rain, cold, snow etc. It also provides protection against dangers which exist as a result of activities at work or when involved in dangerous sports activities. Properties which are important in clothing to protect the body include thermal insulation and moisture.

― Task

1 Look at the photos. Describe the type of characters that the costumes would be suitable for.

Thermal insulation

To prevent heat loss from the body during cold weather, clothing must provide insulation from the cold. This is achieved primarily by the air which is trapped inside clothing. Similarly, in hot weather, the body must be protected from heat. A micro-climate exists between the skin and clothing.

Ventilation is a necessary part of this micro-climate. Ventilation is dependent upon:
- the surface texture of the clothing which in turn is dependent on fibre type, yarn, fabric construction and finishing used
- construction of the garment, for example a tight-fitting garment restricts ventilation
- activity, which includes being exposed to externally moved air as on a windy day as well as movement of the body as in running, doing physical work etc.
- numbers of layers of clothing worn (each layer of which traps air between itself and the next layer).

Moisture absorption

The human body produces moisture in the form of perspiration on the surface of the skin. The amount varies according to the temperature of the environment and the degree of activity taking place. This perspiration has to be absorbed and dispersed by the clothing. This is done by:
- moisture absorption
- **capillary** action.

Air movements affect the microclimate

■ Activity affects the micro-climate

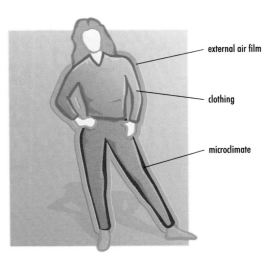

external air film

clothing

microclimate

Insulation from clothing

■ The micro-climate between skin and clothing

Each of these ways depends upon the reaction of a particular fibre to moisture. Fibres are either:
- **hydrophobic** (water-hating) e.g. nylon and polyester, or
- **hydrophilic** (water-loving) e.g. wool and cotton, viscose. These are sometimes referred to as **hygroscopic** (absorbent) fibres.

Moisture absorption takes place when there are low to medium levels of perspiration. The fibres absorb the moisture and diffuse it within the fibres to the outside where it evaporates.

Capillary action takes place when there is a high level of perspiration. The body produces more liquid, which is transported along the fibres (this is the capillary action) through to the outside where it evaporates. This action is sometimes called **wicking** and can be likened to what happens when the wick of a candle takes up wax to keep the candle alight.

The success of both these methods depends upon the rate of evaporation which can take place. For example, if the environment is very humid, evaporation will not take place as quickly as in a dry environment.

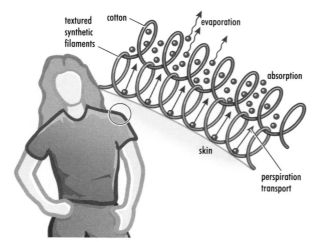

■ How double-layer sportswear works to disperse perspiration

Special fabrics for sportswear

Double-layer fabrics have been developed for sportswear. The inner layer is made of a synthetic fabric from a yarn with good wicking properties, and the outer layer is made of a fabric from a fibre which has good absorbent properties, for example, cotton. Liquid perspiration is rapidly transported through the inner layer to the outer layer where it is absorbed and evaporated.

Weatherproof clothing has specific requirements. It must:
➤ keep out wind, rain and cold (i.e. be weather resistant)
➤ allow perspiration to escape from the body (i.e. be permeable to vapour). The diagram below shows this.

■ Wind and water-resistant but permeable to vapour

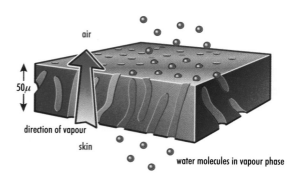

■ A microporous membrane

The three main ways of achieving these requirements involve:
➤ **microporous** membranes
➤ hydrophilic membranes
➤ **microfibre** fabrics with a hydrophobic finish

The use of microporous membranes

These membranes are made up of millions of tiny pores (holes) which are smaller than a water molecule. This means that rain water is kept out. However, the pores are larger than water vapour molecules, which means that the vapour from perspiration can pass through. In Gore-tex® the membrane is made from polytetrafluorethylene (PTFE).

Hydrophilic membranes

A hydrophilic (water-loving) membrane produces a breathable system which can be transfer-coated or laminated as a continuous film on to a wide range of natural or synthetic fabrics, including wool, cotton, nylon and polyester. The membranes take up water vapour from perspiration and transport it through the continuous film to the outside. Permatex® is a hydrophilic polyurethane breathable system made by the Lancashire firm J B Broadley. Permatex® is a solid membrane which has high resistance to abrasion and is very durable.

— Tasks

2 Look at the diagram of the lining system. Explain why it produces weatherproofing properties.

3 Look at the fabric sample of printed Permatex®. Suggest garments for which it could be used.

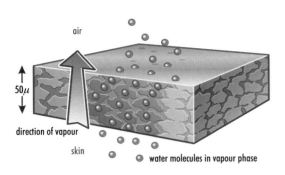

A hydrophilic membrane and the finished product (right)

(Left) A garment made from Trevira-Finesse®

Kendal search and rescue team (above) and a professional golfer (right) wearing garments lined with Permatex® membrane

Micro-fibre fabrics with a hydrophobic (water-hating) finish

Very fine synthetic fibres are used to produce lightly-woven fabrics with very small pores. These are able to resist wetting to a large extent, whilst still allowing vapour from perspiration to pass through. A hydrophobic finish is applied to increase the degree of water resistance. One example is Trevira-Finesse®, a polyester fabric.

— Task

4 Imagine you have been asked by a manufacturer of sports clothes for athletes, in particular skiers and hurdlers, to identify a new range of garments which would be suitable for those particular sports.
   a What are the performance requirements of these sports?
   b What fabrics properties are needed to fulfil those performance requirements?
   c What type of garments would be suitable and, in your opinion, sell well? Why?

Explain the particular features of the garments which meet the needs of the situation.

The case studies which follow are all different examples of designing and making, using textiles. They are all taken from 'real life'. They each show a different type of commercial operation. The studies give information about how textile products and goods are designed, manufactured, marketed and sold. This information will help you learn about and understand how businesses make sure their operations are successful.

Haute couture (high-class dressmaking) is where new lines, trends and styles first appear. These clothes are exclusive and because they are made in very small quantities they are very expensive. Generally, only a small number of fashionable, rich people buy these garments.

This newspaper report, written by Hilary Alexander in the *Daily Telegraph* in October 1996, is about the spring/summer 1997 collection by one designer, John Galliano.

Case study 1: Haute couture

Igniting the creative spark

John Galliano

Last night, in a wine warehouse in Paris, John Galliano showed his spring/summer '97 collection. The 550 invitations were entwined with silver charm bracelets and hidden inside Russian 'matriochka' dolls. The clothes were a cavalcade of colour, passion and beauty. As with everything Galliano has created since graduating from London's central St Martin's School of Art in 1984, it was a vision of a magic world.

He has done the same all through his year's tenure as designer for Givenchy and is now poised to cast his swashbuckling spell over the house of Christian Dior in time for its revelatory 50th anniversary of the 'New Look' in January 1997.

The woman closest to the maverick genius is Lady [Amanda]

Harlech. When she steams over to Paris on Eurostar, she is transformed into confidante-inspiration to one of the 20th century's most gifted designers. This working relationship has endured thirteen years, from two years before she was married.

She arrives at the workrooms in a 'snowflake' Galliano coat over old lace petticoats.

the 'storm' flounce on a gypsy skirt. The hems are trimmed with slivers from Rajasthani saris. A satin corset is pinned atop a canvas toile, with Galliano's felt-tipped instructions scrawled in black. Taffeta rustles, silks glisten – all the fragments which ignite the imagination of the fashion world.

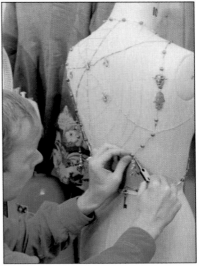

'It all starts with The Word,' she says. 'It could be "kimono", "Fifties diva" or "Empire Line". He sets everyone's imagination alight; ideas erupt, research starts. This season it was "Ukrainian bride", then it became a Russian trapeze artist called Murphy. It's what John does, how he works. What I do is existential. I supply adjectives, research, talk, discover. I'm not a muse. I listen, look, appreciate.'

Amanda is the intellectual foil for Galliano's creativity. Where he designs, she describes; where he sees, she tells stories – turning his clothes into vivid tales of a troupe of tinker-rockers and gypsies around a campfire, and a circus in Outer Mongolia.

Next door a pattern-cutter is scissoring 60 metres of tulle for

*C*lothes with the Jean Muir label are popular, all over the world. They can be seen in large and small stores throughout the world. The following text and photographs are supplied by Jean Muir Ltd.

Case study 2: The Jean Muir Fashion House

Jean Muir – Dress designing is engineering with fabric

The development of the Jean Muir label is a story of success achieved by careful attention to detail, sound understanding of the properties of fibres and cloths and how they react in particular circumstances, and an individual approach to design which takes account of the shape of the human body.

Elegant, classical, wearable clothes typify the Jean Muir approach to design. How is this success maintained? Each collection is distinctive, with features which differ from what has been produced before, but changes are not necessarily dramatic, they evolve gradually. Evolution not revolution is the key to maintaining the support of existing clients and attracting new ones.

There are three collections a year, spring/summer, autumn/winter and cruise (for people taking winter holidays). Each year there are two shows presenting the new collection to international press, buyers and specially invited guests. The show is styled to convey the mood of the collection.

The Collection – its design and production

Colour is the starting point for a new collection. Shade references, anything from a packet of spice to a smudge of pastel crayon, are sent to a dyeing laboratory which produces 'lab dyes' in different cloths and yarns. From these the shades for the season are chosen and sample lengths are ordered.

Additional cloth and yarn are sourced at fabric fairs and directly from mills – some of which will produce patterns and shades exclusive to Jean Muir.

The design team review sketches with the previously chosen cloths in mind and select those which project the mood of the season and which will reflect the needs of the Jean Muir customer.

Toiles (see page 78) are made of the new shapes using blocks which have been developed over the years by Miss Muir and her pattern cutters. These are then fitted on a house model to check that the sketch has been correctly interpreted and that the size is accurate.

Flat patterns are made from card taking fitting alterations into account, and a technical sketch is produced giving all making and stitching details. (Samples are always size 10.)

Samples are cut and made, some shapes in several different cloths. These are then refitted and any further alterations made to the finished garment.

A 'costing' to determine the wholesale selling price of a garment is made by calculating the costs involved in its production, i.e. cloth, lining, interlining, elastic, buttons, zips, thread, labels, and its making price. Added to this is a percentage to cover the company's overheads. The final selling price is determined by the stores who add a further percentage (the retail mark-up) and VAT.

In the days leading up to the show, it is decided exactly how outfits are to be shown and accessorized, models are chosen and outfits allocated to them. Having seen the show, buyers place their orders, deciding which styles, and in which colours and sizes, to carry for the new season.

Production commences – store orders are collated and the exact amount of cloth and trimming required for production is calculated. Thousands of metres of cloth are needed each season. Cloth and trimmings are ordered, giving precise details of colour and finish to the supplier to ensure the production will be to the same high standard as the samples.

At the same time, samples are being rechecked for fit and for the reaction of the cloth to the manufacturing process.

Production patterns and sketches are produced. A first production garment is made by the manufacturer to check their making and the accuracy of the pattern. At this stage alterations may be made to the pattern but only to assist in the manufacture or to correct the size, but not to change the design in any way. Patterns are graded to a range of

seven sizes (8–20), the specification of which has been developed by the company.

Styles are put into production with various manufacturers, but are carefully checked by in-house quality controllers. Production is co-ordinated to ensure that complete outfits are despatched to the stores.

Attention to detail is maintained throughout each process, even the final one, the packing of orders, which Miss Muir considered an art, ensures that the goods reach their destination in perfect condition.

To conclude, it was Miss Muir's belief that it was not until a garment had been sold to a store, then sold to a customer and she had worn it happily that a design could be termed a success.

*B*oden is a mail order company. It has been used in this case study to show how and why such a company is set up, and what has made it such a successful company.

Case study 3: Boden

Why mail order?

The company was set up by Johnnie Boden, for people like him who do not like shopping and would be willing to buy from a catalogue, provided they could be assured that products were of good quality. Johnnie discovered the joys of mail order in New York. He saw catalogues bursting with wonderful products at competitive prices from companies who hadn't forgotten the real meaning of service.

The aim of the Boden company was to provide terrific clothes at great prices to people that appreciate quality clothing. The first steps were:
➤ to make exclusive designs
➤ to use the finest natural fibres
➤ to include style features not available elsewhere
➤ to provide friendly, efficient service, fast delivery and a 'no quibbles' returns policy.

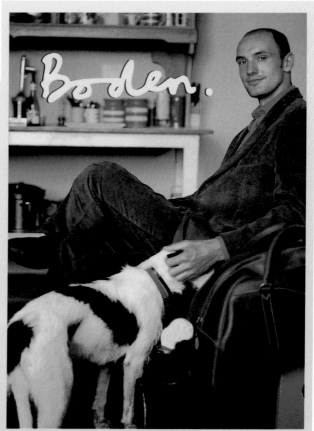

■ 'The essence of Boden'

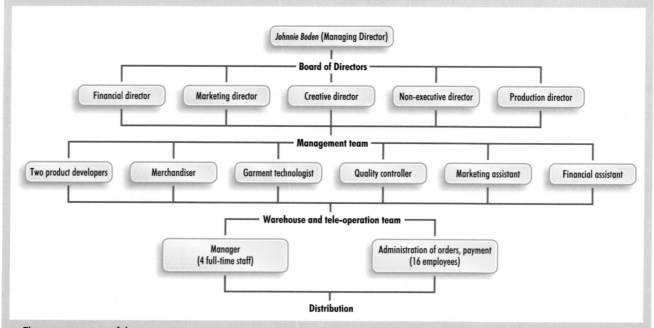

■ The current structure of the company

The first catalogue was produced in Autumn 1991 and had a range of seven products. Since then the company has seen an increase in annual turnover from £2 million in 1991 to £6 million in 1996. More staff have had to be employed and the company has moved to larger premises. There are now over 35,000 customers and the average order value is over £100. Boden's philosophy, however, remains the same, all collections are based on:

➤ well designed clothes that won't date
➤ good-quality cloth ensuring good value for money not cheapness
➤ efficient and friendly service
➤ a 'no quibbles' returns policy.

How does the structure work?

The most important point is that regardless of a person's role and area of responsibility, every individual is involved with everything. That is, everybody is accountable for the smooth running of the company and the distribution of quality products. This is called accountability. In the future an operations director may be appointed. The major responsibility of this person will be to oversee all operations and keep them co-ordinated.

The catalogue

The catalogue is the interface between the customer and the company. It is sent to existing customers and to new people whose names and addresses are taken from a mailing list hired by Boden. The creative director has the responsibility for catalogue production.

The three photos on this page are taken from a spring catalogue. The catalogue for any one season must be available ahead of that season.

How does the company decide what to include in the catalogue?

There are a number of stages in this process.

1 Analysis of the previous two seasons to identify which categories have sold well and which have not, which have made money, and which have not

This is called **merchandise analysis**. 'Number crunching' takes place as a result of this analysis. All the numbers are recorded on spreadsheets and the strengths and weaknesses discussed. 'Winners' and 'losers' are identified. Questions are asked, such as, 'Was the price right?', 'Were fabric and colours right or wrong?' Positive lessons are learnt from this analysis which aids decisions which have to be made about what to include in the next season's catalogue.

2 Reverse of the analysis described in one

The team starts with a blank sheet of paper. Suggestions for garments are made, based on:
➤ a forecast by the marketing people, who predict the rate of response to products
➤ a purchasing budget which indicates what can be spent on production (without which nothing can be done).

The purchasing budget is 'driven' by the forecast of sales for the season.

3 Design developments

The product developers and Johnnie Boden work together on design. The aim is to keep ahead of what is selling, to predict styles, colours and shapes that will be successful. They go on comparative shopping trips, research by looking at magazines and generally have a commercial awareness of what everybody else is doing and whether they can do it better.

Fifty per cent of the catalogue stays roughly the same, for example the velvet jeans shown have proved to be very popular so they are repeated.

The design team visits shows, particularly the main fabric show, *Premiere Vision*, held in Paris, to get fashion ideas. They may have a style in mind first or a fabric might suggest a style. Ranges and designs are discussed, many changes are made to achieve perfection before agreement about the designs to produce is reached.

4 Manufacturing

Boden uses outside manufacturers in two distinct ways:
➤ **fully factored** Boden buys a completed garment from the manufacturer for an agreed price. Boden keeps control of quality because the manufacturer produces the garment according to Boden's specification

■ Velvet jeans from Boden, as modelled in one of their catalogues

➤ **cut, make and trim** (CMT) Boden buys the fabric and pays the manufacturer to make it up to Boden's specification.

Which is better? Fully factored is more easily managed but slightly more expensive. For the manufacturers there is a certain amount of risk because the retailing company could 'pull' a line (say they do not want it any more) and the manufacturer is left with goods not sold and machinery idle.

The CMT method is still used a great deal in the United Kingdom. It can be difficult to manage because the fabric has to be bought, stored and delivered to the manufacturer and this can involve additional costs such as insurance, making out more invoices etc.

5 *Production* 1

The production director works with the design team and has to decide who is going to manufacture the garments. The decision is based on a known relationship with manufacturers, such as the Hebden Bridge Clothing Company who make trousers for Boden (see Case study 5).

A contract is written up for the company, which has been selected. The contract includes a very tight specification for manufacture, prices, delivery conditions and dates. A supplier's manual is issued which lays out the standards which Boden requires.

6 *Samples*

Samples have to be ready for the photo-shoot, for example, in November for the spring/summer catalogue. The samples go to Kenya with the creative director where the photo-shoot takes place. 'Real people' are used to model the clothes because it is believed that this gives an accurate representation of what people will look like in them. The manufacturer must provide samples as shown on the sampling procedure sheet. The **sealed sample** must be perfect and representative of the quality of every garment. It is a point of reference against which quality is checked.

7 *Production* 2

Full-scale production is supervised by the production director who has to check progress and make sure delivery dates are kept. Quality production is checked in the warehouse. At the moment Boden is moving towards 'roving' quality control, which means that controllers will visit production sites during the production process. This is thought to be a more efficient process.

8 *Delivery and despatch*

When the goods are delivered to the warehouse they are:
➤ counted
➤ matched with the original order
➤ checked for quality.

They are then packed and despatched to customers according to orders which have been made. Good presentation is an important feature of packing. Tissue and cardboard boxes with the Boden logo are used and garments are 'flat-packed' and put into polythene bags.

Production in the United Kingdom or abroad?

Like many retailers Boden finds it more expensive to deal with manufacturers in the UK. The reasons for this include the fact that yarns and fabrics produced in the UK are expensive. This is partly due to labour costs and also to the high costs of machinery (e.g. an industrial knitting machine costs as much as £100,000). Boden buys large quantities from abroad but may have a small trial of garments made up in the UK. If the trial is successful and demand for the garments grows, the larger scale of production may be carried out abroad. A typical comparison of prices for a fully factored garment may be:
➤ abroad £9
➤ UK around £16 to £18.

The firm makes healthy profits, not huge ones, but any extra costs of production have to be reflected in the selling price.

Case study 4: Jeans

Jeans have a long history. They can be traced back to the 16th century when sailors from the Italian port of Genoa wore trousers with a particular cut. The word 'jeans' comes from 'Genovese'. The cloth the trousers were made from was a special fabric woven in the French city of Nîmes. This heavy hard-wearing fabric was called 'serge de Nîmes' and this is where the word 'denim' comes from. So denim jeans were 'born' many years ago. At a similar time in history the same type of cloth was being worn by fisherman in Dhuga, India. These tough trousers were called 'dungarees', hence another modern garment was born. The original colour of denim was natural stone, but eventually the leaves of the Indigofera plant

DENIM FABRIC - HOW IT'S MADE

STEP ONE - Cotton bales are opened, cleaned and blended to ensure the greatest possible fibre uniformity. The fibres are separated and foreign matter removed.

STEP TWO - Cotton is fed into carding machines, where the fibres are combed to make them parallel. They are then formed into a card sliver.

STEP THREE - The card sliver goes onto drawing frames, which further parallels the fibre. The sliver goes onto the roving frame where the diameter is reduced, and twisting into something like yarn takes place.

STEP FOUR - The spinning frame takes the roving, reduces it to the necessary size and then twists the fibres into proper yarn. The filling yarn goes to the denim looms and the warp yarns to the processing areas.

STEP FIVE - The spooler takes the warp yarn and transfers it to a package called "cheese". Cheeses are put into a warper, where they are wound on beams to be dyed. The warp yarns thus supply the indigo colour in the eventual fabric.

STEP SIX - The warp beams are dyed on an indigo range.

STEP SEVEN - The strands of dyed yarn are separated and wound onto a beam. These beams are combined at the slashers to form the warp, which goes to the loom. Warp yarns are strengthened on slashers by coating them with a layer of starch called sizing.

STEP EIGHT - The warp and filling yarns are ready for weaving on high-speed automatic looms. The warp yarn runs lengthwise, the filling yarn crosswise in the fabric.

STEP NINE - Cloth inspected, finished, re-inspected and put in cartons or rolls for shipment.

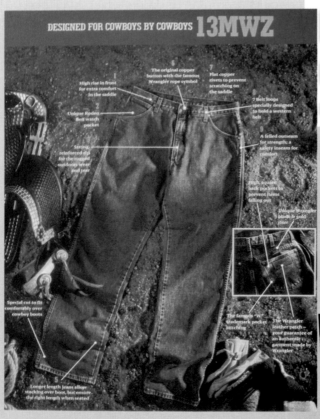

were used to dye it a deep blue. Synthetic Indigo was produced in the late 1800s.

The flow diagram on page 102 shows how denim fabric is made. The flow diagram on this page shows the steps involved in the making of Wrangler jeans.

Quality Control

For more than 40 years Wrangler has been ensuring strict Quality Control through a precisely-worded warranty attached to all merchandise. Throughout Wrangler manufacturing units across the world, Quality Control managers keep constant watch on the many fabrics and garment components that pass through their plants.

Wrangler garments are always made from the best materials available, and the Quality Control system was established to make certain the company's image is not allowed to slip.

At the Wrangler UK Falkirk plant laboratory for example, a permanent staff of technicians test out fabrics and finished garments under carefully controlled conditions.

Everything is studied for shrinkage, fading, tensile strength, crocking and stiffness — and just about everything else it can be subjected to in daily wear and tear.

In wash test, all denim, corduroys and cotton mixes are generally washed at 60 degrees, and tumble-dried in warm air no less than five times. Following a two-hour 'condition' period the swatches (small squares of fabric) are measured micrometrically for shrinkage and fading, and carefully graded. Anything not passing the test is not used in production.

Our INSTROM machine measures the tensile strength, pulling the cloth in every way possible at a power far greater than anything the garment could be subjected to in the market place.

The testing does not finish there however. A yarn count is carried out by the naked eye to ensure that all Wrangler specifications have been met by our suppliers.

The Wrangler Quality Control operations throughout the world remain unmatched.

1. Design - The first step is the creation of the design and style ideas. This is done by a team of designers who know what fashion trends are and who work with all European merchandising and marketing executives to satisfy the demands of each individual fashion market.

2. Sample - The next stage is to see how the design looks when made into a garment. A prototype pattern is cut, and the making up of the sample garment will indicate the different manufacturing techniques required - and ultimately, the cost of the finished item.

3. Patterns - The prototype pattern is then given to a specialist computer programmer, who looks at the different pattern pieces to see how the jigsaw can be most efficiently laid down on the fabric.
There are 10 basic pattern pieces to make a pair of jeans.

1. Left front	5. Hip pockets	9. Back riser
2. Right front	6. Inside of front pocket	10. Belt loop
3. Left back	7. Facing of front pocket	
4. Right back	8. Waistband	

Individual sets of pattern pieces are made in every size that a particular style of jean will be offered in.

4. Piece Goods (the fabric) - The fabrics used for making jeans - denim, cotton twills, corduroys etc - are made by large textile mills and are shipped directly to the respective jean plants.

5. Marking and Cutting - After the pieces are on the cutting table in a 'layout' a long sheet of paper is placed on top and held in place. The computerized tracer then applies the pattern layout worked out by the computer programmer onto the sheet. A computerized cutter then slices through the multiple layers of fabric. Accuracy is paramount, as a mistake would be extremely costly! The trace is an insurance against the computer 'going down'. If it does so, then a mechanical cutter can take over the task without ruining the vast quantities of fabric - or delaying the production process.

6. Bundling - After the fabric is cut to the exact pattern size, the small pieces are put into bundles ready for transfer to the sewing department.

7. Sewing - Most of the work in making jeans is sewing the pieces of fabric together. There are dozens of different sewing operations. Here are some of them:
- assembling the smaller parts of the jeans such as: a) putting pockets together; b) making belt loops; c) making back pockets ready (applying 'W' stitch & leather patch)
- attaching pockets
- sewing main seams on legs
- sewing on waistband
- attaching buttons on band
- sewing bottom hem
- attaching belt loops
- sewing in zip
- attaching rivets or sewing bar-tacks at stress points
- attaching woven labels giving size and washing care*

*(this is an important item. Every pair of jeans made by Wrangler has a permanent sewn-in printed label that tells the consumer the exact size of garment. The label is designed to last for the life of the garment).

8. Quality Checks - Because people, machines and even computers make mistakes sometimes, it is important to remove any item that may have got through with a mistake. Special Quality Control checkers are assigned to this job, and the jeans are inspected all the way through the production process and again when they are finished.

9. Final Steps - After the jeans are sewn up and inspected, they are laundered to a chosen colour standard and pressed, and tags are attached to waistbands and back pockets to help the consumer identify sizes, styles and fits.

10. Final Steps - packaging and warehouse - Sophisticated warehousing techniques are used to ensure that minimum time is spent between receipt of orders and dispatch of goods to retail consumers. The whole system is computerized!

Case study 5: The Hebden Bridge Clothing Co.

The Hebden Bridge Clothing Company is another success story. It was set up in 1982 by four people who were made redundant by a local manufacturer. Barbara Bannister, Mary Cooper, Veronica Hartley and Keith Powell pooled their redundancy money and set up the company. Today they form the board of directors. The textile industry in the UK has been seriously reduced as a result of recession which means that, to be successful, a company must be very sure of what it can do well. The four directors brought to their company a variety of expertise and experience and a commitment to manufacturing high-quality products. It is this combination which has made them successful.

The Hebden Bridge Clothing Company source and use high-quality cloth; customers specify the weave they want. They use stock lines from weaving mills unless an individual customer wants a cloth outside stock lines. They manufacture high quality garments for a number of retailers including Boden, Cordings and Hackets. The trousers shown are made for Boden (see Case study 3).

What contributes to their success?

There are a number of factors:
- Courtesy calls are made by buyers to discuss future requirements.
- Plans are made twelve months ahead to make for smooth organization and the meeting of delivery dates.
- Flexibility of operation – the company produces garments made by CMT and fully factored methods according to what the buyers require.
- Garments are made specifically to order. This means that only the number of garments ordered are cut out and made up, stock is not hanging about waiting to be sold.
- The most efficient and productive methods for manufacture have been developed.
- High standards of quality control are in operation throughout manufacture.

■ Trousers made for Boden

Case study 6: Marks & Spencer

Marks & Spencer plc have a worldwide reputation for quality products and for keeping up with new developments in fibre, fabric and garment production. Their range of thermal underwear illustrates this reputation and sells extremely well.

The label on this page shows the fibres used for the thermal range, by type and percentage. In addition, size, colour and care instructions are given.

■ A label (front and back) from a thermal garment

Yarn production for thermal garments

1 Preparation

Polyester and viscose are delivered to the factory in bales weighing around 300 kg. The bale opener machine breaks the material into small tufts. The tufts are accurately weighed and mixed to achieve the required blend. The material is then formed into a lap, ready for carding.

2 Carding

The blend is fed into a series of cylinders containing saw-toothed wire rollers where the fibres are individually separated before being formed into a web of fibres. This is condensed into a soft rope known as a sliver.

3 Draw frame

A number of slivers are drawn from the carding machine and reduced so that the fibres become blended together. Irregularities within the sliver are eliminated and the fibres become parallel.

4 Speed frame

The slivers are reduced by further drawing out to the diameter of thick soft thread. By this time the sliver is so thin that it must be twisted to strengthen it before it can be wound onto a bobbin.

5 Spinning

Drafting rollers thin down the yarn to its final thickness and insert 'twist' to strengthen it. The yarn is then wound onto a ring tube.

6 Winding

The winding process:
- uses electronic clearers to remove any spinning faults within the yarn
- imparts a small amount of wax onto the yarn to reduce friction, (this is only for knitted yarns)
- forms one large package, suitable for processing by the knitter or weaver, from a number of small ring tubes.

The finished yarn is used to produce seamed and seam-free fabrics for thermal garments.

Seam-free garments

The first stage is the knitting of bleached yarn into fabric. This is done on a circular knitting machine. Each garment size requires a different size of knitting machine. Photo A shows the yarn being fed into the machine at a controlled rate. Thousands of individual knitting needles knit the fabric in a spiral fashion. The tube of fabric is drawn down through the bottom of the machine and rolled around a beam.

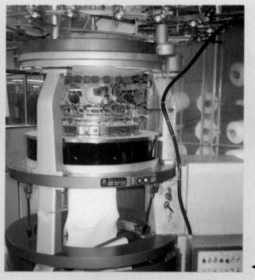

◀ A

There are enough machines in the factory (see photo B) to produce a constant supply of knitting to meet the needs for the season. The machines are operated around the clock by trained technicians.

The tubes of fabric are fed into a steam relaxation machine (photo C) which uses steam to relax the fabric and prevent shrinkage

B ▼

C ▲

D ▲

E ▲

when the customer washes the finished garment. The steam also dissolves the threads joining the individual garment panels so that these can be separated easily.

The garment blanks are taken to the making-up units where machinists carry out the final garment assembly.

Seamed garments

A circular knitting machine is again used, producing a wide tube of fabric. This is then cut open and used as flat fabric.

The fabric is laid on a special table, very smoothly, several layers thick with plastic sheeting in between each piece of fabric. The plastic prevents the fabric from slipping when it is being cut.

Garment shapes are then automatically cut out to the required shape by a computer controlled process using a band knife (photo D). This produces garment blanks which are taken to making-up units where machinists carry out the final garment assembly (photo E).

■ An example of a finished garment

— *Case study task* —

The case studies are included in this book to help you learn about commercial production using textiles.

Use the headings on the right to describe what you have learned from the case studies about making sure a business is successful.

a Design
b Manufacture
c Marketing
d Selling
e Company organization
f Personnel

Four case studies

The people featured in the case studies in this unit use textiles in very different ways. The first three are all designer-makers who have a good commercial understanding of the market which exists for their products. They prepare proposals for clients, interpret briefs and produce beautiful end-products. All three were described in a magazine article as 'shining examples of today's trailblazers whose work is bold, challenging and innovative in the use of colour, texture, shape and stitch'. The fourth person is a designer of weaves for a very well-known silk-weaving company.

They are included in this book to provide sources of inspiration for and methods of making various products which you could use to help you in design and making tasks in school.

Case study 1: Jilli Blackwood

Wall-hangings, waistcoats and wacky top hats are Jilli's speciality. She traces her sense of colour, texture and pattern to the house she lived in as a child. It was an extraordinary 1900s house based on a Roman villa, which had been decorated by a family of Italian craftsmen. Jilli remembers lovely mosaic floors and ceilings, lots of fabrics and Afghan rugs. Jilli uses ecru silk bought from a wholesaler in different weights and textures and dyes it at home. Sometimes new colour ideas come to her from the splashes on the floor, which suggest surprising combinations. Finished fabrics are created by layering, stitching, clipping, cutting and pulled thread work.

■ Jilli and her daughter, Naomi are wearing some of Jilli's designs

Jilli's route to becoming a successful designer-maker

LECTURING & TEACHING
1996	Glasgow School of Art Lecturing & Teaching
1993	Dundee School of Art Lecture
1993	Glasgow School of Art Lecturing and running summer School
1993	Edinburgh Embroiderers Guild
1992	Renfrewshire Embroiderers Guild
1991	Glasgow Embroiderers Guild
1990	Tribal Textiles from South East Asia Collins Gallery Strathclyde University
1989	Demonstration Glasgow Art Gallery & Museum
1989	Visiting Lecturer Victoria & Albert Museum London
1989	Visiting Lecturer Scottish College of Textiles Galashiels
1989-93	Glasgow school of Art Textile department

PERMANENT COLLECTIONS
1992	Embroiderers Guild Hampton Court Palace
1990	Glasgow Museum & Art Gallery Kelvingrove
1989	Aberdeen Art Gallery - Commissioned Textile

PRIVATE COLLECTIONS - LARGE WORK
1996	Cornfields U.K.
1993	Silk Feathers 1993 U.K.
1992	The Fourth of July 1991 U.S.A.
1991	Silk Evocation 1990 U.S.A.
1990	Tartan Runner 1990 London
1988	Caledonia 1988 Spain

TRAVEL
1992	Travel Busary, Santa Fe U.S.A. British Council
1990	Travelled to Thailand visiting weaving villages in association with Oxfam

OTHERS
1995 Royal Mail Aerogram 150 years Glasgow School of Art
... Television programme Home Show
... ...ion panel of Craft Council Slide & Permanent Collection
...
...ign fabrics and
...
... of Glasgow school of

1990	"Textiles" Exhibition Glasgow Art Gallery & Museum
1990-91	Touring Exhibition of Accessories, Norwich Art Centre + other venues
1990	Scottish society of Woman Artists R.S.A. Edinburgh
1989-90	G.S.A. Embroidery Group "Crossing the Border" Collins Gallery Strathclyde University Glasgow
1988-89	Glasgow Society of Woman Artists - Exhibit regularly
1988-89	New British Embroidery Exhibition, touring nationally
1988	Quilting Exhibition, Aberystwyth Art Centre
1988	Paisley Museum Centenary Exhibition
1988	Fashion & Art / Art & Fashion, The Fine Art Society Glasgow
1988	Three Strands Exhibition, Glasgow Embroidery Guild
1986-87	Jugend Gestalet Munich Germany
1987	"Glasgow Style" Glasgow, Amsterdam, Berlin
	Young Creators Exhibition Design Council London & Touring

BOOKS
A Cornucopia Of Cushion	by Susie Johns Published Quarto
Crafts (International)	Edited by Martina Margretts Published Thames & Hudson
The Applique Book	Juliet Bawden Published Mitchell Bearley Ltd
Ideas in Weaving	Ann Sutton Published 1989 Front Cover Textile Design
British Fabrics	Kylie Sanderson Columbus Press Ltd 1988

PUBLICATIONS
Glasgow Herald	Mistress of the Tactile Textile May,20th 199...
Country Living	Material Girls September 1993
Craft	Review of Crossing Borders Exhibition Jun...
Glasgow Herald	"Mistress of the Ragamuffin Topper Nov 19...
Fiber Arts USA	New Works "Silk Feathers" 1991
International Textiles	Interior No 3 1990 Profile "Cut-Offs"
Elle	Scottish Talents Aug 1990
Scam	Antiques of Tomorrow Sept 1990
Crafts	Contemporary British Weave Review June...
Arts Review	Contemporary British Weave London Rev...
House & Garden	Exhibition Review Feb 1990
House & Garden	6 Contemporary Textile Designers April 1...
Sky Magazine	Fruit of the Loom Talent section Feb 198...
Craft	Look of the Old Craft Council June 1988
Craft Work	Spring Issue No 19 1988
House & Garden	Decorators Notebook Aug 1987
Italian Vogue	Fabric Lengths & Scarves April 1987
Observer Magazine	29th June 1986
Glasgow Herald	25th June 1986
Scottish Field	Cover Insert Oct 1986
Scottish Field	Accessories March 1986
Scottish Field	Accessories Nov 1985
Scottish Field	Harris Tweed Competition May 1995

JILLI   BLACKWOOD
24 CLEVEDEN ROAD
GLASGOW
G12 OPX
Tel / Fax 041-334 6180

1965	Born Glasgow
1982 -86	Glasgow School of Art
1983 -86	Specialising in Embroidered & Woven Textiles

AWARDS
1990	Glasgow Society of Women Artists McCreadie Award
1989	Semi - Finalist, International Textile Design Contest, Tokyo, Japan
1987	Selected for inclusion on Craft Council Slide Index London
1986	Business Course at Stirling University Graduate Enterprise
1986	Graduated 1st Class B.A. Honours Art & Design
1986	Coats Paton Embroidery Award
1985	Bursary from Weavers Association
1984	Prize winner Harris Tweed Competition

CRAFT FAIR / TRADE SHOWS
1988	Time Out Live, Olympia, London
1987 & 88	Chelsea Craft Fair, Kings Road, London
1986	Fabrex, Olympia, London, Design Council Section "Texprint"
1986	Scotfree S.D.A. Commonwealth Institute London
1986	R.S.A. Degree Show London

SOLO EXHIBITIONS
1991	Textile Exhibition, Gatehouse Gallery Glasgow
1990	Textiles The Craft Council Shop Victoria & Albert Museum London
1989	Showcase Aberdeen Art Gallery & Museum

SELECTED EXHIBITIONS
1996	Sanderson George &Peach Gallery Christmas Exhibition Yorkshire
1996	Textiles Rufford Craft Centre
1995	100 Years of Embroidery and Weave at Glasgow School of Art touring Hampton Court Palace
1995	Raw Materials Contemporary Scottish Textile Exhibition, Galashiels, touring
1993	"Crossing Borders" Textile Exhibition C.C.A. Gallery Cambridge
1992	Running Ridge Gallery, Santa Fe, New Mexico, USA
1992	"Out of the Frame" Craft Council National Touring Exhibition
1991	"Textiles Today" Bury St Edmunds Gallery
1990	Textile Exhibition Phillips Auction Rooms Oxford
	"Stitched Textiles" Embroiderers Guild Commonwealth Institute London

Jilli Blackwood's step by step guide to planning a wall-hanging

PLANNING A WALL-HANGING

STAGE 1:

- Find a source of inspiration, i.e. landscape, architecture, ceramics, historical costumes.
- Draw from your subject matter using different media, e.g. pastels, inks, oil pastel, watercolours, paint, tissue and coloured papers.
- Experiment with implements which create interesting marks and textures, such as toothbrushes, forks, knives and paintbrushes.
- Build relief and texture into your drawing. Be as imaginative as possible. There are no rules.

STAGE 2:

- Research your subjects through secondary sources such as books, paintings magazines and other embroidery techniques.
- Look at artists who have produced work similar to your chosen theme. This will help you to expand your thinking and allow you to realize the many different ways one source of inspiration can be interpreted.

STAGE 3:

- Plan the design on paper. Refer to your drawings at all times for composition, proportion, shape, line, texture and marks.

STAGE 4:

- Research different types of fabrics such as cottons, silks, linens, wools, velvets and synthetics. Look for the different properties in various types of fabric, such as lustre, smoothness, texture and weave. Choose fabrics which excite you.

STAGE 5:

- Bring colour to your work by dyeing or painting onto fabric. Refer to your drawing so that your relationship in your paper work is continued into your sampling and through to the final wall-hanging.
- Fabrics and yarns can be random dyed using wax or wrapping. This is called resist dyeing. Over-dyeing fabrics also help to personalize them.

STAGE 6:

- Sampling can take place at any point during the creation of the design. This like creating your own dictionary of techniques which can be referred back to when working on any future designs.
- Allow yourself to be free at this stage as you were during your preliminary drawings.
- Refer back to your drawings for shape, line and texture and use techniques you are already familiar with, i.e. drawn threadwork quilting, couching, handstitching, machine embroidery, burning, etc. Allow your drawings to dictate the texturing and relief in your sampling. Expand your ideas at all times.

STAGE 7:

- Finally bring all your ideas to the final wall-hanging.

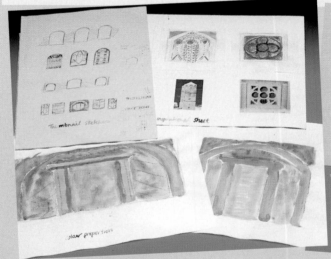

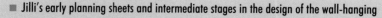
- Jilli's early planning sheets and intermediate stages in the design of the wall-hanging

■ Jilli's final planning sheet. The story-board for the wall-hanging

fabric samples

■ Examples of Jilli's wacky top hats and techniques

Case study 2: Lorna Moffat

Lorna Moffat is artist in residence at Highworth Grammar School in Kent, as well as being a self-employed designer-maker of textile products. Lorna works on commissions with private clients and interior decorators. The photos below show Lorna, her cushions and some details from her designs. Influenced by traditional techniques such as the 'mola' work produced by South American Indians, and mid-17th century 'stump' work, Lorna has invented her own methods of achieving depth of surface pattern using a modern sewing machine.

The flow diagram shows Lorna's approach.

Lorna's designs are inspired by – amongst other things – stained-glass windows, wrought ironwork and medieval tiles. Inspiration for Lorna's first commission came from the machinery used in the distilling industry. The commission was from Teacher's Whisky and was for a wall-hanging for the company's conference room.

Sandwich of between five and seven layers of different coloured fabrics.

↓

Design sketched in tailor's chalk on top.

↓

Lines of design followed round with machined stitching

↓

Layers trimmed away with scissors to reveal colours underneath.

■ Lorna Moffat and some of her products

Designing a textile panel for school

The banner project below was carried out at Highworth Grammar School. The brief to students was to design a textile panel based on the school motto 'Reach for the Stars'. All the designs shown are by year 9 and 10 students.

The stages in development of the panel

Photos 1 and 2 show early experiments with white fabrics, paper and glue. Photo 3 shows experiments with fabric, design and machine stitching.

   Photos 4–7 show examples of mola and appliqué work which were used to generate ideas for the panel.

Designing cushions

Lorna's brief from a client was to create a collection of six cushions for the living room interior shown in the photo.

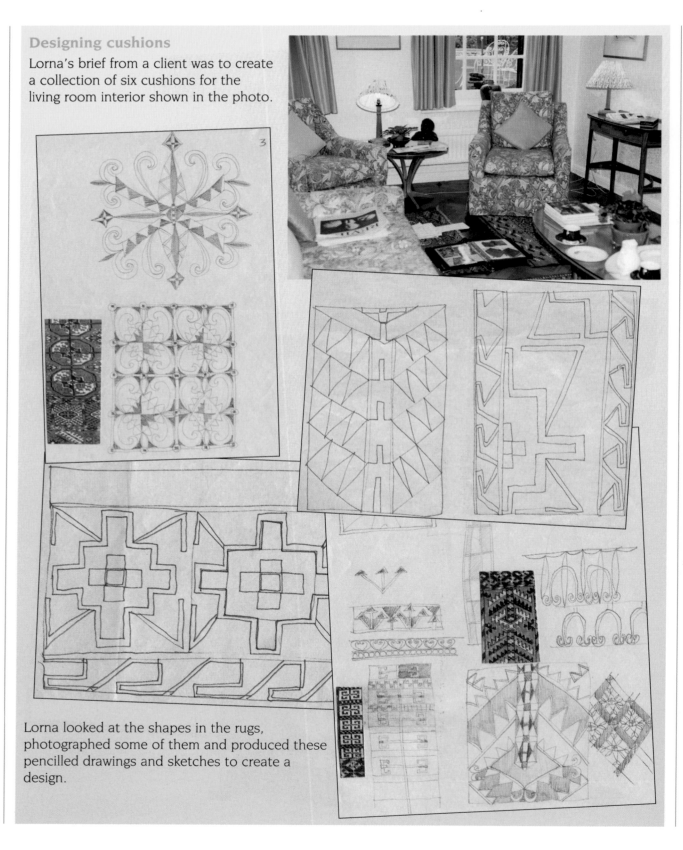

Lorna looked at the shapes in the rugs, photographed some of them and produced these pencilled drawings and sketches to create a design.

The Mola and appliqué cushions shown below were inspired by the colours and designs of Turkish rugs.

Investigating self-portraits in fabric

The next sequence of illustrations shows an investigation into self-portrait in fabric. It was carried out by Jodie Driscoll of Highworth Grammar School. The investigation illustrates an approach which could be used to develop textile products such as wall-hangings, cushions and other textile items which could be sold in the shop of an art gallery or museum. This investigation could be used as inspiration for such a brief.

The sequence of the investigation

■ Illustrations 1, 2 and 3 show studies in sketchbooks, evoking emotion in colour. (Illustration 3 shows texture in a collage.)

■ Illustration 5 is a self-portrait in tissue, paper and glue.

■ Illustration 4 is Vincent Van Gogh; it is an example of an artist who evokes emotions and moods in his work.

■ Illustrations 6 and 7 are self portraits in fabric using small snippets of fabric glued to a calico base then machine and hand stitched to add definition.

Case study 3: Annie Sherburne

Annie Sherburne is a textile artist who has made a name for herself as one of the country's most innovative textile designers. Some of her work in felt is shown in Unit 3.3 (page 57).

The felt wall-hanging shown below is part of Annie's Crafts Council Collection. It is called 'Funky Fossil' and measures 3 m by 2 m (9 ft by 6 ft).

Annie describes designer-makers as people who have ideas as starting points for products which they describe and explore and then plan for making. She is shown in the photo against a felt rug/room divider, which was a private commission.

Here is Annie Sherburne's advice about approaching and carrying out design-and-make tasks and investigations.

Initial inspiration for my work comes from all sorts of places; the leaves in autumn, sunsets, reflections, music, colours, even seemingly dreary places, rainy, grey days, a torn poster, abstract shapes which prompt initial ideas.

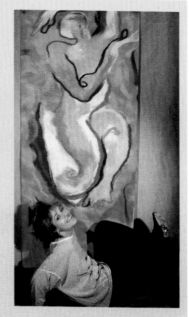

One idea usually leads to another, but the real art is communicating what you think is special about the idea to other people. To be a successful designer other people have to like what you do enough to pay you to do it!

The first stages of making are exploratory. There are hundreds of ways of constructing textiles. It is important to learn some of the techniques such as spinning, weaving, felt-making, tapestry, printing, batik, tie-dye, knotting, plying, shibrori, quilting, braiding (kumitimo), garment-making, millinery, natural dyeing and so on.

I usually start with materials. It is sensible to use what is available and local. I then try out ideas and shapes by drawing them. A key word is 'inventive'. I analyse the materials and experiment with their properties.

One task I would suggest is to take one fabric, explore its properties and then find ten different ways of connecting or constructing it. For example, take some cotton sheeting, tear and cut it into strips, some along the straight grain and some on the bias (diagonal) and note the properties of the pieces of fabric in their new form. The diagonal pieces will stretch, which gives the fabric an ability to drape. It is this property which is used to perfect the 'engineering' in tailoring where a sleeve is eased into place and sewn into the main body of a jacket, thus creating sharp and perfect control of the fabric in garment form.

Next try pleating the cotton. Also try slashing it at regular marked intervals. (Shopping bags are made by slashing plasticized sheeting which then expands when objects – the shopping – weigh it into shape.) Experiment generally with the fabric; knot it, sew it, cut it into spirals and sew one spiral to another along the longest edges.

If your task involves darning or weaving, explore the way the weft thread is passed through, over and around the warp threads. Free weaving and knotting can create a fabric of interest and beauty by use of colour and/or surface relief. I made the jewellery shown with bead weaving, woven onto a painted bejewelled shape.

A sense of achievement and satisfaction in the process creates new impetus. The textile itself is the greatest delight, the journey involved in making the product is also enjoyable. Too often we can get disheartened by the question, 'What is it for?'. In some cases the end-use is 'down the line'. Every textile we use has been designed and processed many times before we come to it – your input as a creative designer will be appreciated.

If your input is developed commercially, it could be used by a fashion designer for clothes or for use on walls, on furniture, in art galleries, and so on.

An example of ideas, techniques and technology working together is to be found in a Japanese company called 'Nuno'. Their products can be seen in Liberty's store in London's Regent Street.

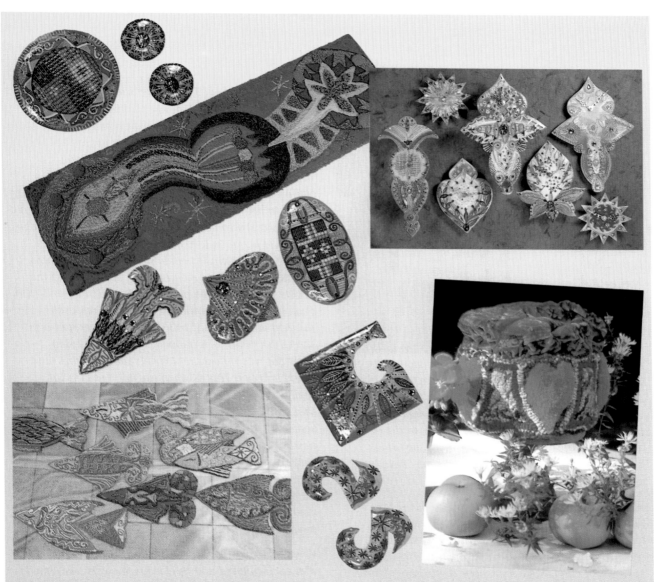

Contemporary designer-makers like me make a range of products which we sell. We are small-scale enterprises and often work alone. The onus for invention is with us. We have to develop the product, find a market and sell the work in order to survive.

My current work in textiles is tufting using a hand-held gun, painting silk ties and producing fine bead work. In each of these areas I am using colour and pattern to create art works that can be used. The tie is usually the only decorative element in a man's business clothing. It tends to have a style all of its own. It is a communication from the wearer and has an acknowledged psychological message.

One of the first times I remember choosing colours was at the local wool shop. Here the potential palette was up on shelves covering a wall. I could make colour associations, see the harmonies and put the colours together to make a new hat, leg-warmers, gloves or whatever. It is a good idea to lay out your potential palette whether it be in fabric, wool, beads, paint, crayons etc.

Many of the most successful makers combine a solid grounding in technique with a fascination for new possibilities. Learning basic techniques will always stand you in good stead.

*B*arbara Milligan is a Member of the Chartered Society of Artists and Designers. She is design director of The Gainsborough Silk Weaving Company. In the passage below, Barbara tells below how she came to the position she now holds.

Case study 4: Barbara Milligan

My interest in textiles in general seems to have begun at school in about 1965 when I was in the sixth form. Our embroidery teacher got together a group of girls, all fairly keen on embroidery, and took us to London for a week, staying in a training college and visiting the Victoria and Albert Museum each day. We made a particular study of Opus Anglicanum or 'English Work' which was the ecclesiastical embroidery done in this country in the Middle Ages and exported. In the evenings we went to the theatre, and for me I think probably my interest in the textile arts may have been sparked off by those visits to the V&A.

When I left school I chose to attend the local Art College in Great Yarmouth to take a two-year foundation course, then decided to specialize in textiles. I must have been rather half-hearted about it at first as I can clearly remember the textile lecturer telling me that if I wasn't prepared to work hard he wouldn't bother with me.

Our college was just starting to do courses of the Society of Artists and Designers (now known as Chartered Society of Designers), and I became the first student to be assessed for a Licentiateship of the Society in printed textiles.

After a further three years, in which I worked non-stop, I showed my work of printed fabrics and wallpapers and was assessed by Humphrey Spender. It was quite exciting, and apparently a first for the college at the time.

After that of course, I was faced with the almost impossible task, like all newly-qualified students, of actually finding a job. This was even more difficult than getting the qualification. I went for numerous interviews which met with no success and then, in desperation almost, applied for a job in the local library as an assistant. Two years were spent stamping books in and out, until I began to think, 'Well this is not what I worked so hard for.' Finally, a local magazine in one issue had a feature on a silk-weaving mill at Sudbury (The Gainsborough Silk Weaving Company). It was not until several months later, after reading the article, that I took the plunge and wrote a letter to the firm. It was a shot in the dark, as I had not even touched on weaving at college. All my work had been screen printing. As it happened, the then design assistant was thinking of leaving and I couldn't have timed it better. That is when the interest in textiles really began to take off, with weaving. I realized then that with printing you are applying a design to something already produced, but with weaving you are making the fabric and building in the design at the same time. As it happened, I couldn't have chosen a more prestigious company to apply to, as the fabrics we produce go to all kinds of palaces, art galleries, stately homes and of course, the most important Royal residence, Buckingham Palace.

When I started the job in 1972, all the design work was hand-painted and the jacquard cards were hand-cut which was very labour-intensive. Now, 23 years later I work on a computer screen which has revolutionized the process, and speeds everything up. Even the reproduction of very old historic fabrics with all the unevenness and individuality of a hand woven piece can be carried out on a computer. I feel now that I am very lucky to have had the opportunity to work with these types of fabrics. Also it has given me the chance to be trained in using the very latest design equipment which is advancing all the time.

It also must mean that it is always worth having a go at something which is not necessarily exactly what you have trained for.

The Gainsborough Silk Weaving Company

Gainsborough is continually developing in order to maintain and
extend its market and to enable the company to continue to
produce, economically and profitably, the high-quality merchandise
for which it is internationally known. This development involves the
increased use of electronic looms and computerized systems. The
following pages give more information about stock ranges and the
design and manufacturing processes involved.

The samples shown are examples of stock ranges. Notice that the measurements of the design repeats are included. Stock lines are those fabrics woven using weaves which are always available. Some clients want special effects and colour combinations which means that a special weave is designed and the yarns are dyed to a particular specification.

Some of the information printed in the brochure is shown below. The photos on this and the opposite page show the use of computers in designing weaves, plus the sequence and processes involved in dyeing and weaving at The Gainsborough Silk Weaving Company.

Dyeing and weaving

■ The yarn is dyed in hanks. The hanks are turned to ensure even dyeing

Designing

■ Claire Everest B.A.
A designer at Gainsborough

■ Applying weaves stored in the computer onto colours in the design to create the weaving effects

■ The dyed yarn is wound onto bobbins

STRIPES

GAINSBOROUGH CAN PRODUCE STRIPES IN ALMOST ANY COMBINATION OF COLOURS, WIDTH, QUALITY AND WEAVE.

QUALITIES OFFERED INCLUDE:
A) COTTON
B) COTTON AND SILK
C) COTTON AND FLAX
D) SILK AND WORSTED
E) SILK

WEAVES CAN BE CHOSEN FROM E.G.
A) TABBY
B) SATIN
C) TWILL

STRIPE CONFIGURATIONS
E.G.: WIDE, NARROW, MIRRORED, IRREGULAR. MOST VARIATIONS CAN BE REPRODUCED TO YOUR REQUEST.

COLOUR
ANY COLOUR CAN BE SELECTED FROM OUR LIBRARY OF CUTTINGS OR MATCHED TO YOUR OWN COLOUR SAMPLES.

THE DESIGN DEPARTMENT WILL PRODUCE A CARD WRAPPING OF ANY STRIPE LAYOUT FOR VISUAL APPRECIATION OF COLOUR AND SPACING. THIS AVOIDS THE EXPENSE AND TIME OR PRODUCING A TRIAL WEAVE AND WILL AID YOUR PRESENTATION TO YOUR CLIENT.

■ Examples of four stock lines from the Gainsborough brochure

Dyeing and weaving

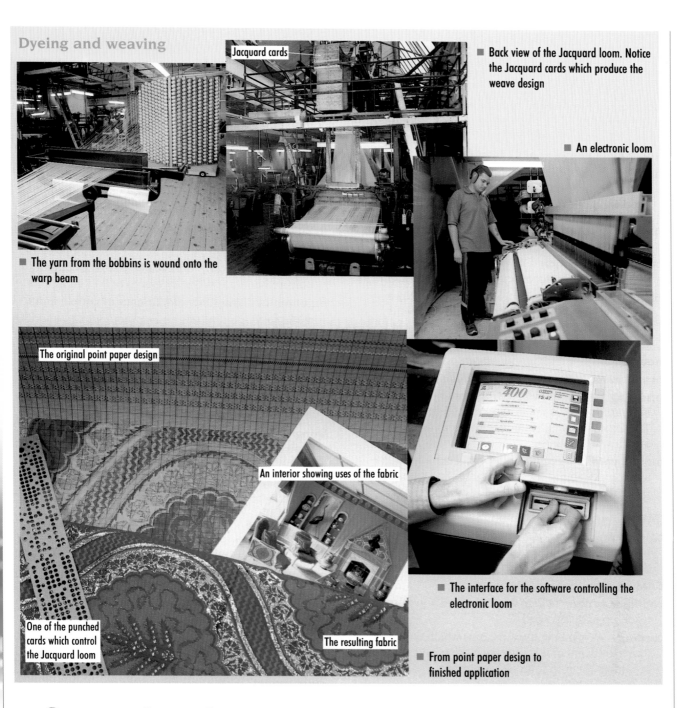

Jacquard cards

■ Back view of the Jacquard loom. Notice the Jacquard cards which produce the weave design

■ An electronic loom

■ The yarn from the bobbins is wound onto the warp beam

The original point paper design

An interior showing uses of the fabric

One of the punched cards which control the Jacquard loom

The resulting fabric

■ The interface for the software controlling the electronic loom

■ From point paper design to finished application

— Case study task

The case studies are included in the book to help you develop and generate inspiration, ideas and methods of producing items from textiles. Use the headings on the right to describe what you have learned from the case studies.

a Inspiration sources
b Ideas for products
c Methods of production
d Techniques

Glossary

acetate   A type of regenerated fibre.

acrylic   Synthetic textile fibre.

aesthetics   Appreciation of beauty. Philosophy of the beautiful or of art.

anthropmetric design   Equipment and work spaces designed to the fit the dimensions and movements of the human body.

apparel   Clothing and/or dress.

appliqué   Work cut out from one material and laid upon and fixed to the surface of another material to produce a decorative effect.

batik   A method of applying colour and pattern to fabric using wax.

bespoke production   Where garments are made for individual clients according to size and requirements.

block printing   A method of printing whereby a design is cut into a flat surface, to which dye is applied and then the flat surface (the block) is pressed onto the fabric.

bouclé   A knot, loop or curl effect.

brand name   The registered trade name of a product.

brushing   A process where the fibre ends of a fabric are passed over a series of wire-covered rollers. This produces a fluffy surface and a thicker, softer fabric.

bulked yarns   Yarns which have been made bigger whilst maintaining normal elasticity and extensibility properties.

CAD   Computer-Aided Design.

calendering   A process whereby a fabric is passed between heated rollers, under pressure, to produce different effects, e.g. glazing or Moiré.

CAM   Computer-Aided Manufacture.

capillary action   Where moisture (and liquid) are taken up and absorbed.

carding   A 'combing' type process which pulls fibres to make them parallel with each other and then separates them to form a sliver (rope).

complementary colours   Those colours that are directly opposite each other on the colour wheel.

conformance   How well a product meets the specification.

cotton   A natural fibre made from the plant seed of the cotton plant.

cotton boll   The seed case of the cotton plant.

couture fashion   Exclusive, highly individual example of fashion.

cybernetics   The science of how systems organize, regulate and reproduce themselves.

demographic trends   The study of figures relating to deaths, births, diseases etc.

dimensional stability   The degree of elasticity or the measurement of how much a fibre will shrink or stretch.

disassembly   Taking things apart to see how, and from what, they are made.

drawing and drafting   Reducing the thickness of slivers of fibres.

dry spinning   The process whereby a polymer solution is extruded into a stream of warm air which evaporates the solvent and solidifies the filaments.

Elastane   A 'stretchy' fibre made from segmented polyurethane. Lycra® is an example.

ergonomics   The study of efficiency of people in the work place.

extensibility   A fibre's resistance to breaking.

felt   A type of non-woven fabric.

fixation   The 'fixing' of a dye to make sure it is fast.

flax   A blue-flowered plant which produces a fibre from which linen is made.

flying shuttle   A shuttle propelled by hammers in a loom. A shuttle is the device which carries the weft thread across warp threads in weaving.

formability   The degree to which a fabric can be formed into shapes.

generic name   The name of the fibre as detailed in BS4815 (the glossary of generic names for manufactured fibres).

gimp yarn   Two fine yarns which are twisted in opposite directions with a third yarn held in an S-loop.

ginning   A process that separates cotton fibres from the seeds. It is also used in the production of manufactured fibres.

haute couture   High-class dressmaking.

heddle   A frame used in weaving which allows groups of warp threads to be lifted up and down.

hierarchy of needs   The order in which people want and need things, as defined by Abraham Maslow.

high bulked yarns   Bulked yarns made from a blend of fibres (i.e. those with a high tendency to shrink, blended with those with a low tendency to shrink).

hue   The name of a colour, e.g. blue or yellow-green.

hydrophilic fibres   Water-loving fibres, e.g. wool or cotton.

hydrophobic fibres   Water-hating fibres, e.g. nylon.

hygroscopic fibres   Absorbent (water-loving) fibres.

Jacquard loom   Invented by Joseph Marie-Jacquard. A system of weaving where each individual warp can be lifted in a pre-planned sequence using punched cards which move on a belt above the loom.

just-in-case   Items are kept in stock in case they are needed.

just-in-time   Stock levels are maintained in such a way that stock is available just at the time it is needed.

kitemark   A quality assurance label which appears on a product that has been subjected to regular routine testing during production.

knop yarn   Two yarns twisted together, one of them being wound round and round to form a lump or knop.

laminated fabrics   Two or more fabrics stuck together or fabrics stuck (or bonded) to foam or plastic.

lap   A sheet of fibre.

lay planning   Planning how pattern pieces are to be cut from a piece of fabric to ensure efficient use of fabric and good results in the finished garment.

linen   A natural fibre produced from the flax plant.

make through   Where skilled machinists carry out the main construction of a garment and other machinists do the overlocking, button holes, etc.

manufactured fibres   Fibres that can be regenerated (e.g. viscose) or synthetic (e.g. nylon).

market research   Methods used to get information about what consumers want to buy, what their expectations of a product are and what they think of the product.

melt spinning   A process whereby polymer chips are put into a bath and melted before being forced through a spinneret. The melted polymer is extruded into cold air which cools the melt and solidifies the filaments.

micro-fibre fabrics   Very fine synthetic fibres are used to produce lightly-woven fabrics with very small pores. These resist wetting to a large extent but still allow perspiration (i.e. water vapour) to pass through.

microporous membranes   Membranes made up of millions of tiny pores which are smaller than water molecules but larger than water vapour molecules. The effect is that rain cannot penetrate but perspiration (i.e. water vapour) can pass through.

modal   A type of regenerated fibre.

natural fibres   Fibres produced from natural sources, e.g. from vegetable and animal sources.

needle felt   A non-woven fabric made by stitching layers of fibre webs together with a needling machine.

niche marketing   Producing products for narrowly-defined market needs.

nomadic   Groups of people who move from place to place.

non-woven fabrics   Fabrics made by webs of fibre which are bonded together by structure, sticking or melting.

nylon   A polyamide (synthetic) fibre.

pilling   Tiny balls of fibre which appear on the surface of some fabrics, e.g. wool or synthetics.

plied yarns   Two or more single yarns twisted together.

polymer   Several identical units joined together.

primary colours   Yellow, red, blue.

production patterns   Patterns which show seams, grain lines and other relevant symbols.

progressive bundle system   Where garment pieces are taken to the machinist who is going to carry out a particular operation.

quality assurance   Checking conformance at every stage of production, manufacture and retailing of a product.

quality control   Checking procedures at every stage of development to make sure a product meets the specification.

quilting   Two plies of fabric with wadding in between and sewn together in straight lines or by following a particular pattern to produce a decorative finish.

range meeting   A meeting where design, marketing and production teams discuss the development of a new product or range of products.

rapid response   A system which makes the processes involved in production, distribution and marketing efficient and speedy.

recycling   Using something again, rather than throwing it away.

ring spinning   The final process in cotton yarn production. The roving (unfinished yarn) is passed through a hole (called a pot eye) and a small ring (called a traveller) which add twist to strengthen the yarn before it is wound onto the bobbin.

screen printing   An image is cut out of a thin sheet of film which is then placed over a screen made from a frame covered with a fine fabric. Dye is pushed through the screen and the image (design) is printed onto the fabric underneath.

scutching   A process which cleans and rolls fibres into sheets (laps).

secondary colours   Orange, green and violet.

selvedge   The firm edge placed in the warp at both ends of a fabric.

shirring   A method of gathering and disposing of fullness using elastic thread.

silk   A natural fibre produced by the larvae of the silk moth.

smocking   A method of gathering and disposing of fullness using decorative stitching.

spinning   Where fibres are twisted into yarn.

spiral yarn   A two-ply yarn twisted with another thick, soft and twisted yarn.

spun-bonded fabrics   Webs of fabric which are fused together by methods such as heating and sticking with adhesives.

S-spun   Yarn spun with an anti-clockwise twist.

story-board   The method used by designers to present collections.

tenacity   The strength of a fibre.

tertiary colours   Yellow-green, blue-green, blue-violet, red-violet, red-orange, yellow-orange.

textile recovery   Another way of describing the recycling of textiles.

toile   A garment modelled in muslin or calico.

Toyota Sewing System   Where machines are laid out in a U shape, serviced by about ten skilled operators who work together on one bundle at a time.

twill   A pattern of diagonal lines made when each warp yarn lifts over (or remains under) more than one weft yarn.

Unit Production System (UPS)   A system where there is a power-driven loop which has workplaces spaced at regular intervals.

value (of a colour)   The lightness or darkness of a colour which describes how near it is to black or white.

Velcro   Two woven polyamide tapes which stick together to form a secure fastening.

viscose   A regenerated fibre.

warp knits   Fabric made using yarn loops in a vertical direction – the fabric being held together by the interlocking vertical loops and loops on alternate sides.

weaving   The production of cloth/fabric by interlacing a single thread over and under a series of parallel threads.

weft knits   Fabric made using a single yarn which forms loops across or around a circle.

wet spinning   A process whereby a polymer solution is extruded into a bath which contains chemical which neutralize the dissolved fluid and solidifies the filaments.

xanthation   The adding of Carbon Disulphide to change cellulose into a fluid.

Z-spun   Yarn spun with a clockwise twist.

Index